PATCHES

An inspiring collection of short stories

by

Barbara A. Robinson

Barbara A. Robinson asserts the moral right to be identified as the author of this work.

Cover design: © 2022 Melinda De Ross. All rights reserved.

Copy editing: Effrosyni Moschoudi

This is a work of fiction. Names, characters, places, and incidents either are the products of the author's imagination or are used fictitiously, and any resemblance to locales, events, business establishments, or actual persons - living or dead - is entirely coincidental.

To my grandmother, Beulah Beatrice Dark

To Justine my friend at WEAA

May you continue to bless others with your spirit and obvious love of people

Barbara H Robinson
2-25-2022

Contents

PREFACE

When I was a child growing up in Alabama, I lived with my grandmother, whom I called "Mama." Mama made the most beautiful handsewn quilts I had ever seen. They were like a painting. Each pattern on her quilts told a story which prompted her to give each quilt a theme. Mama made a quilt she called the "Wedding Band," each patch on that quilt represented two entwined wedding bands. One of her quilts was called the "Christmas Tree", each patch on that quilt was in the colors of red and green. Mama had a quilt called the "Family Quilt" where each patch was made from scraps of material she saved from clothes she'd made for her family.

In the 1930s and 1940s, chicken feed, flour, corn meal, and supplies that were sold in bulk were packaged in heavy woven material similar to the heavy-duty material from which dungarees and overalls are made. Printed on the sacks were designs of flowers, birds, animals and various other things. When the sacks were empty, Mama washed them and used that material to make clothes for her family. Shirts were made for my mother's brothers, and skirts, dresses and blouses were made for my mother and her sisters. With the leftover scraps of material Mama made quilts and those quilts she called "Sack Cloth Quilts."

Some scraps of material were given to Mama by white folks that they collected from the seamstresses and tailors who made clothes for them and from members of their families. They were white folks whose laundry Mama did each week, washing and ironing their clothes for one dollar and twenty-five cents for a week's load of clothes for an entire family. They knew in return they would receive a handmade patch-work quilt of the kind of quality that could not be purchased in stores.

Mama would give those quilts to her family and some she sold to neighbors and to the white folks for whom she washed and ironed clothes. I wish I had known how valuable handmade quilts would become years later. I would have saved those that Mama made. When I became an adult and lived in Baltimore, Maryland, each year the mayor would display homemade quilts in the lobby of the city hall. Newspapers and television stations would cover the event and a stream of people would come to see the week-long display. This book is like Mama's quilts. It contains patches of life written together into a fine quilt. Life is full of different scenes, different scenarios, different events, different life styles, different moments in time and each moment is a gift from God.

My life is like the patches that my grandmother used when she made her beautiful quilts.

One year, in the rotunda of the city hall in Baltimore, Maryland, the mayor of Baltimore allowed an organization to display a collection of quilts handmade by various individuals. I looked at the display of quilts and thought about Mama's handwork. The quilts on display had various designs and messages interwoven into the designs of the patchwork. Those quilts reminded me of my life that consists of patches of different scenes, different scenarios, different moments in time, moments to remember and cherish.

Throughout this book, the reader can escape from the humdrum of life through imagination and fantasies. You, dear reader, can imagine being whatever and whoever you want to be. Some of the stories contained herein are "patches" of my life. Others are patches from my imagination. I love to write short stories. I like to tell a story, end it, and then begin another one. There is so much to say about so many things in life.

In this book I have included ghost stories that grownups told us kids at night when the Georgia moon and stars were shining so brightly, they lit up the night like African brush fires. These were the nights when we didn't have to go to school the next day. Once supper was finished and dishes were washed, we children sat on the front porch steps quietly listening to the low voices of grownups telling stories about ghosts, goblins, strange aspirations, and about the Bible, too. The grownups told us kids the stories their grandparents had told them when they were kids too, growing up in the South.

I have fond memories of my childhood in Georgia and in Alabama. I enjoyed the elders of the neighborhood telling ghost stories to us children. Each week, my sister Sandy and I took turns washing supper dishes. When it was my week to wash the dishes, I hurried to finish so I could go outside. Sometimes, we would lie about whose turn it was to wash the dishes. Each of us wanted to be the first outside to pick the best seat for our weekly ghost stories, always scrambling for the seat next to the adult storyteller.

In Georgia, we sat on the Johnsons' steps next door, under the clear, blue, starry, moonlit, Georgia sky. When I was in Alabama, sometimes, we would sit outside with my grandfather, whom we called "Papa," and my grandmother, whom we called "Mama" or the lady next door to Mama's house, whom we called "Mama Doshie." Mama Doshie was a kind and friendly person, who lived next door to my grandmother in Alexander City, Alabama. She lived to be more than one hundred years old. When I was a little girl, I would go over to her house and sit with her on her front porch and listen to her tell stories about her life. I wasn't related to her but still, the children in the small neighborhood and I called her, "Mama Doshie."

When I was in Georgia I would sit with the other neighborhood children, listening to Mr. Johnson tell ghost stories. The later the hour got, the sleepier we children got, the more afraid we became, and the scarier the stories sounded. After all, everyone knows that witches and ghosts travel at midnight, especially when there's a full moon.

Cecelia's father, Mr. Johnson, and her older brother George, took turns telling "scary" stories. The Johnsons' house was so close to our house that we could jump from our front porch onto theirs. When Mr. Johnson told ghost stories, we kids thought they were true. Sometimes, the stories sounded so real that we were afraid to go to sleep at night, fearing the "bogeyman" or the monsters under the bed would get us. Of course, when we got older, we learned there was no such thing as a "bogeyman." But we sure did believe he existed when we were kids.

The radio was the major source of entertainment during the 1940s and 1950s. VCRs and video games were not yet available back then. Television was just coming out and most families in my neighborhood didn't have one. Sitting on the front porch at night, listening to the grown-ups tell ghost stories was more entertaining than listening to the radio. The elders of the neighborhood were like the elders of the village. It was an African custom to sit around the campfire in the evenings and listen to the elders tell stories to the young folks.

Sitting outside at night in Georgia and Alabama, under the magnificent Southern moon, during the warm summer nights was my utopia. A gentle breeze was blowing, somewhere in the distance crickets were chirping and frogs were croaking. Once in a while, the leaves on the trees and bushes made a rustling sound as the night wind gently kissed them. That will always be a part of my beautiful memories of home. That calmness and peaceful feeling with the night sounds was a typical Southern night.

I enjoyed writing this book, though I tend to hurry and change subjects often—being a typical Gemini. I hope you have fun reading these stories because I sure did have fun writing them.

Not only does this book contain stories that are patches of my life, it also contains a compilation of stories from my imagination and from stories shared with me by friends and colleagues I met along my journey through life. Like a fine glass of wine, I savored those stories to preserve history and used some of the lessons from the past as teachable moments. This book contains some of the "ills" of life, and unfortunately, some of the "realities" of life, too. So, dear reader, enjoy this book, this intricate patchwork of life...

The Power of a Smile

I am a mother of three children, ages fourteen, twelve, and three, and I have recently completed my college degree. The last class I was required to take was Sociology. The teacher was absolutely inspiring. She had qualities that I wish every human being had been graced with. Her last project of the term was called, "Smile."

The class was asked to go out and smile at three random people and document their reactions. I am a very friendly person and always smile at everyone and say "hello!" So, I thought this project would be a piece of cake. Soon after we were assigned the project, my husband, youngest son, and I went out to McDonald's one crisp March morning. It was just our way of sharing special playtime with our son.

We were standing in line, waiting to be served, when all of a sudden everyone around us began to back away. My husband also began to back away. I didn't move an inch... and an overwhelming feeling of panic welled up inside of me as I turned to see why they had all moved.

As I turned around, I smelled a horrible, dirty-body odor, and there, standing behind me, were two men. By the way they were dressed and their body odor, I assumed they were homeless. I looked down at the shorter of the two men, who stood closer to me. He was smiling. His beautiful sky-blue eyes were bright and friendly, and he looked as if he were searching for acceptance from the people in line.

I looked at him and smiled.

"Good day!" he said as he counted the few coins he was clutching. The second man fumbled with his hands as he stood behind his friend and kept his eyes glued to the floor. He appeared unwilling to look in the faces of the annoyed customers. As I looked at the second man, I realized he was mentally challenged and the blue-eyed man with him was acting as his caretaker.

I held back my tears as I stood and looked at them, and, all the while, I was aware of the obvious feelings of rejection harbored by those who were standing in line with them. The young lady at the counter asked the man with the bright eyes what they were ordering. "Coffee is all, Ma'am," he replied in a polite voice.

He laid the coins on the counter in front of the young woman, then stepped back, seemingly in anticipation that she would hesitate to pick up the coins. It appeared that coffee was all the two men could afford. They just wanted to sit in the restaurant and warm up, so they had to buy something. The blue-eyed young man walked to a table in the far corner of the restaurant. The second man followed, his eyes still directed to the floor.

Then I really felt it. The repulsion of the other people in the restaurant was so great I almost reached out and embraced the little man with the blue eyes. I could tell he felt it too. Since I was the only person who had not backed up, I noticed that all eyes in the restaurant were set on me, judging my every action. My husband and young son also waited to see what I would do next.

I smiled at them all and asked the young lady behind the counter to give me two more breakfast meals on a separate tray. I took the trays and carried them to the table where the men were sitting and placed the trays on the table. I gently placed my hand on the blue-eyed gentleman's cold hand, and he looked up at me with tears in his eyes.

"Thank you!" he said, trying hard not to let the teardrops fall.

I leaned over and patted his hand. "I did not do this for you. God is here working through me to give you hope." I tried hard to fight back my own tears. But as I walked away to join my husband and son, I couldn't hold back the tears any more. When I sat down, my husband smiled at me. I could tell he, too, was misty-eyed.

"That's why God gave you to me, honey; to give me hope," my husband said. He leaned over and kissed me on my cheek. My son got out of his seat and, with a look of pride shining in his eyes and a big wide grin on his face, hugged me ever so tightly.

"I love you, Mom!" he whispered. My husband and I held hands for a moment and at that time, we knew that only because of the Grace of God we were able to give back. That day showed me the pure Light of God's sweet love. I returned to college, on the last evening of class, with this story in hand. I turned in "my project" and the instructor read it.

"Can I share this?" she asked.

I slowly nodded my head, giving her approval to read it to the class.

"Attention, class! I want to share something with you that contains a lesson for us all." When she had their attention, she began to read my story about my visit to McDonald's restaurant and that is when I knew that we as human beings seemed to all share the need to help people. In my own way, I had touched the people at McDonald's, my son, my husband, my instructor, and every soul that shared the classroom on the last night I spent as a college student.

I graduated with one of the biggest lessons I would ever learn. We are all God's children and you can feel a smile.

The moral of this story is, treat others as you want them to treat you. Sometimes, a smile is all it takes to make someone's day.

Telephone Call to Heaven

I sometimes have strange dreams. I often dream that I'm flying. Once, I dreamed that there were buildings in the sky, whole cities of them. Another time I dreamed that my mother came back to visit me to help me put an end to my self-imposed pity parties about not having spent more time with her while she was still alive. Then, one day I started wondering which had been the strangest dream of all. I decided it was a dream where I'd made a long-distance call to Heaven to tell God about my troubles here on Earth. In my dream, I dialed Heaven and Archangel Gabriel answered the call:

"Hello, this is Gabriel."

"Hello, Gabriel, this is Barbara Robinson. I'm calling to speak to God."

"Hello, Sister Barbara. I was standing by the Pearly Gates blowing my trumpet when I heard the phone ring. It's good to hear from you. I have a new tune called Hallelujah, Anyhow. I'll play it for you on my trumpet when you come home."

"I need to talk to God and tell Him about my troubles. Sometimes, I have to moan. Sometimes, my burdens get so heavy I don't think I can go on. I've lost my job. I'm living in the projects, I'm on welfare and my children's Christmas toys were stolen. My gas and electric bill are so high I can't pay it. I can't afford food. Yesterday, the sheriff put an eviction notice on my apartment door. My husband is in jail. I need to talk to God."

Gabriel fell quiet for a moment, then said, "Just a minute, I'll go find Him for you."

I held the line and waited, anxious to tell God my troubles. I heard someone pick up the telephone.

"Hello, is this God?"

It was my mother's voice on the other end.

"Hello, Baby. Gabriel told me you were on the line. How are my grandchildren? Tell them I love them. Tell them to stay in school and get an education. Tell them to stand tall and proud. Tell them when they're at the end of their rope to tie a knot in it and hold on. Give one end to God and He'll hold them up. When you get home to Heaven, I have a new Holy Dance to show you. I know I couldn't sing or dance when I was on Earth, but here in Heaven, every note I sing is a melody. God has given me a new voice."

I laughed when she said that. I remembered how she couldn't carry a tune in a bucket when she was on Earth; she couldn't even hum in tune.

"Mother, you don't know how much I miss you. I look at your picture all the time and wish you were here. It's hard down here on Earth. Satan is having a party here and it's getting worse every day. I need to talk to God."

"Hold on, Baby, I'll get the Master for you. Don't hang up. It was good talking to you. I'll be glad to see you when you get home. I love you, Baby."

"I love you too, Mother."

I tried unsuccessfully to hold back the tears. I was glad to hear that she was happy with God. I'd always known that she was in Heaven. I waited, and started to get impatient because God was taking too long to answer my call. Then I heard my grandmother's voice.

"Hello, Baby. Your mother said you were on the telephone line. It's been only yesterday since I last heard your voice."

I was perplexed by her statement about it being "only yesterday."

"Mama, how can it be only yesterday since you last heard my voice? It's been over fifty years since you passed away."

"That's how long it seems to you, Baby. But here in Heaven, it's only been a matter of hours."

"Mama, I haven't forgotten what you taught me. You taught me that I can be whatever I want to be if I want it badly enough. You taught me that the dictionary is the only place where success comes before work. You taught me that my condition does not have to be my conclusion. But, Mama, you don't know how bad things are here on Earth. Things are worse than when I used to lay my head in your lap and go to sleep. I'm trying to call God, but I've been holding on for a long time. Please see if you can find Him for me. Maybe He doesn't have time to talk to me. I know He has the whole world to protect."

"God doesn't have too much that He can't handle," my grandmama said. "I know it's hard for you on Earth. I've heard about all the things that are happening there. But God is still in charge. I'll go and see if I can find Him. Don't give up hope."

I waited and I heard someone pick up the receiver. I thought it was God, but then I heard my daughter Jeanette's voice. She had died when she was seventeen days old.

"Hi, Mother," she said, "I miss you. I asked Grandma to tell me about you. I wish I could have gotten to know you before the Master called me home. But He had work for me to do. I've learned to use my wings. When you get to Heaven, I'll teach you how to use yours."

I began to cry again.

"Daughter, I miss you! I wish I could have seen you grow up. What a joyous time we'll have when I get to Heaven. I'm excited that all of you, my loved ones, are there waiting for me. But I've been trying to reach God."

"I'll get Him for you," my daughter said. "Tell my sisters and brother I love them and I wish I could have met them on Earth, but God had other plans for me. Tell them I'll see them when they get to Glory. I've been bragging to all the angels about my two sisters, who are my triplet sisters, and about my older sister and my baby brother. I can't wait to see them. But I have another surprise for you. Someone else wants to say something."

"Finally, God is going to get on the line and speak to me!" I mumbled. But when the other voice said "Hello" it wasn't God. It was Jerry, my husband.

"Hello, Baby. I've been watching over you and the family. God made me your guardian angel. I am so proud of how you have kept our family together, and I am especially proud of what you have done with your life. You are a great role model for our children and grandchildren."

"Jerry!" I screamed into the telephone. "It's so good to hear your voice. You have no idea how much I miss you. There are so many things I want to say, things I wish I had said before you left, things that I couldn't bring myself to say before you died."

He seemed to understand my hesitation.

"It's okay, Baby. You can let go. I'm in a better place now."

"Jerry, I wish I had said 'I love you' more often. I love you so much."

"I know that."

He had a way of saying "I know that" and it always made me laugh. I missed hearing those words.

"I'll wait for you. When your work on Earth is completed and Father brings you home, I'll be waiting for you. Now, I'll get Father. Just a minute."

I waited a few minutes more, still holding the telephone and waiting to speak to God. Just when I thought I heard God's voice, Saint Peter came to the phone.

"Hello, this is Saint Peter. Are you being helped?"

"Hello, Saint Peter. I'm waiting to talk to God. I've been holding on for a long time. My grandmother said that my mother was flying around Heaven, singing. When I heard that, I laughed. I know that everybody must have been wearing earplugs, because my mother can't sing."

"God doesn't listen to how fine the voice is," said Saint Peter. "God just wants to hear your praises. All praises sound like music to God's ears. So, it's not the voice He's interested in, it's the praises."

"I've been holding on for a long time. It's a long-distance call. I may not be able to pay for it."

"Just hold on, Sis. God's not too busy to talk to you. I know you've been waiting a long time to talk to Him, but hold on. He might not get here as quickly as you think He should, but He's always on time. God's time is not your time. He might not come when you call Him, but He's never late. He'll be with you in His own time. Don't be impatient; just wait," said Peter.

Then, finally, God picked up the telephone.

"Hello, my child. I know you're having a hard time, but know that I am with you always. Your troubles may bend your back, but I won't let it break. I know you have to cry sometimes, but know that I will dry your tears. I know that sometimes the way is dark, but know that I am the Light. I know that sometimes you may see only one set of footprints and you may think that you're walking alone, but know that at those times, I am carrying you. I know that a lot of doors have been closed to you, but know that when one door closes, I'll open two. I'll open doors in places where you didn't know doors existed. I know there are many obstacles in your way, but know that I am the way maker. I know there are many mountains to climb, but know that if you have faith in Me, I'll move those mountains. I know there are good times and bad times in your life, but know that I am the same always. I know that sometimes you feel alone and unloved, but know that I love you enough to let my only Son die for your sins."

God's voice was soft and comforting. It was almost like the sound of music.

God said, "Don't worry, Daughter. When I sent you to work with my people who couldn't help themselves and you followed my instructions without questions and without protesting, you were paying your bill. When I told you that I needed someone to send on a mission and you said, 'Here I am, Lord, send me,' it was paid. When My Son died on the cross, it was paid. When you returned to Me ten percent of what I gave you, it was paid. When you took the time to visit the sick and the shut-in, it was paid. When you looked beyond the faults of others and saw their worth, it was paid. When the way was rough and you said, 'Hallelujah, anyhow,' it was paid. When you had faith in Me although you couldn't see Me, it was paid. When you got on your knees and said, 'Thank you for being God all by Yourself,' you were making a down payment on your bill. When you heard gossip and you didn't repeat it, you were making a down payment. When I whispered your name and you said, 'Hush, hush, somebody's calling my name,' and you were still and obedient, you were paying your bill. When you gave Me praise during the good times and the hard times, you were paying your bill. So, My Child, your bill was paid by your deeds. Your prayers are already being worked on. Your troubles are being changed into triumphs, your obstacles into opportunities, problems into possibilities and chaos into challenges. Your bill is paid in full."

Standing on God's Promises

Once upon a time, there were two farmers. One was named Brown and the other was named Adams. For years, Brown envied Adams because Adams had more land than him. On several occasions, Brown had tried to buy Adams' land but Adams had refused to sell. Greed and jealousy were gnawing at Brown's ego. He couldn't think of anything else except how to get Adams' land. So, he devised a scheme to kill Adams and take his land.

There was an old well in Brown's backyard that he planned to fill in with dirt. He had already bought the dirt and it was in a pile next to the old well. Brown decided he would invite Adams over to his house and bury him alive in the old well. Brown figured that if Adams disappeared, his widow wouldn't be able to keep up the taxes on their farm and he would be able to buy it from her at a cheap price. It was a set up.

So many of us, dear reader, try to hurt others and end up getting hurt ourselves. We don't see things as they are, but as we want them to be. Adams should have seen through Brown's lies but he didn't. They had been neighbors for many years but Brown had never invited Adams over to his farm before to socialize. Therefore, when Brown extended such an invitation that time, it should have sent a red flag to Adams to be cautious. Adams knew that Brown had always wanted his property. He should have known that Brown couldn't have changed overnight. But Adams trusted him and thought he had changed. So, he went to his house.

The two men sat at the table laughing, talking, drinking corn liquor, telling jokes and acting friendly until late that night. When Adams was ready to go home, Brown suggested that he leave by the back door and take the short cut across his property. He said that he would walk with Adams to continue the joke he had started to tell. It was dark in the backyard and Adams couldn't see the deep hole that was once a well. Brown put his arm around Adams' shoulders, laughing and talking, and trying to distract him from seeing the hole. As they walked past the old well, Brown pushed Adams into it. Then Brown started hopping around like a rabbit, laughing and shouting, like a mad man.

"I got you now. Ha, ha, I got you now. Soon your land will be mine, all mine. I knew I'd git ya!" he shouted.

Adams had fallen into the deep, dark hole that was just wide enough for him to stand up in.

"Please don't let me die like this. I'll sell you my farm if you just help me out of this hole. Please, Brown, don't kill me! I have a family. You can have my farm at a cheap price. Please don't let me die like this. If you help me out, I'll give you my land. Please help me," Adams begged.

But Brown didn't believe him.

"No, no! You're trying to trick me. I got you now. Soon, I'll own all your property and, after you're dead, your widow won't be able to pay the taxes, and I'll be able to get the land at a fraction of the cost."

Feeling excited at the prospect, Brown started shoveling dirt into the hole to bury Adams. "No one will find your body. I'll say you left here and then I'll suggest that a wild animal must have dragged you away."

Adams tried again but couldn't get Brown to relent, so he started praying. The hole was too narrow for him to kneel to pray, so he clasped his hands before him, lifted his head unto the heavens, closed his eyes and prayed. As Brown shoveled the dirt into the hole, it fell in Adams' face, but he brushed it off, turned his head to keep the dirt out of his eyes, and kept on praying.

Brown threw another shovel of dirt into the well and began to laugh. The dirt fell on Adams' head and shoulders. Once again, Adams brushed the dirt off and kept praying. The dirt started to pile up around his shoes, then covered them, so he shook the dirt off and stood on top of it.

More dirt kept falling into the hole, and Adams kept brushing it off his shoulders, his clothes and hair. He stood on top of the dirt and kept on praying. He lifted his eyes to the heavens and talked to God.

"Father, please help me. Please don't let me die like this," Adams prayed.

Brown kept on shoveling dirt into the hole and laughing with glee at the thought of owning all of Adams' land.

Adams was now praying silently so that farmer Brown couldn't hear him. "Lord, You promised You would answer my prayers," he whispered. "You said that if I had faith the size of a mustard seed I could move mountains. You promised if I prayed and never doubted, You would bring me out of trouble. You promised if I prayed in secret, You would reward me openly. You promised to never forsake me. You promised to make my enemies my foot stool. Lord, I'm standing on Your promises. I believe in Your promises. I have faith in Your promises. Please don't let me die like this. Father, please help me!"

All the while, Brown kept on shoveling dirt into the hole. Adams brushed it from his clothes, then bowed his head to keep the falling dirt from his eyes and he kept on praying. Every time the dirt fell onto the ground he stood on top of it. This went on until the pile of dirt was almost gone.

"The hole must be full now and Adams should be buried," said Brown to himself as he stood in the darkness.

He went closer to peer down into the hole to see how much more dirt he needed to shovel, and as he approached the old well, he saw Adams stepping out of the hole, brushing dirt off his clothes and from his head.

"How did you do that? You should have been buried under all that dirt I shoveled. I've been shoveling dirt for hours. There's no way you could have dug yourself out," said Brown.

"I stood on God's promises, and stepped out on His Word. Don't you know that one plus God is an army? Not only will you not get my land now, but you'll lose yours too, for attempted murder," said Adams.

Leaving a shocked Brown behind, Adams hurried home and reported to the police what Brown had done. The evidence was there to support Adams' complaint. His footprints were still visible on top of the pile of dirt in the well.

So, my friends, when people shovel dirt on you, such as gossip, betrayal, back-stabbing, lies, and deceit, just brush it off; ask God for help and step out on His promises.

Things Are Not Always as They Seem

Two angels were traveling along a long, dark road in the physical form of two women. They had been traveling all day, on an assignment from God to help Mankind. When night came, weary from walking, they stopped at the home of a wealthy family and asked if they could spend the night. The family didn't know the women were angels. They looked like poor village women. The wealthy family didn't want to provide them with any assistance. But, fearing the women would go back and tell the villagers about the family's refusal to help women in distress, the family reluctantly provided them with minimum help.

When the angels stopped at the house, the family was just sitting down to eat supper. Although they had plenty of food, enough to share, they didn't offer the angels any. The wealthy family was rude, condescending, snobbish, and refused to allow the angels to sleep in one of the mansion's empty guest rooms. Instead, the angels were given a thin blanket, no pillow, and a small space to sleep in the cold basement of the mansion. As the angels made their bed on the hard, cold, stone floor of the basement, the older angel saw a hole in the basement wall and repaired it.

"Why do you help someone who doesn't want to help others?" the younger angel asked.

"Things aren't always as they seem," the older angel replied.

The younger angel looked puzzled at the response from the older angel but she didn't question her any further.

They went to sleep, and it proved to be an uncomfortable experience on the hard, cold floor. The next morning, the two angels got up, and without being offered breakfast, they set out on their journey. When night fell the second time, the angels stopped at another house and asked if they could spend the night. This was the home of a poor, but hospitable, farmer, his wife, and two small children. The farmer's family didn't have much food, but they gladly shared what little they had with the angels. After they had eaten, the farmer and his wife offered their bed to the angels.

"You appear as though you have been traveling a long way and you look weary. It's not much, but please, sleep in our bed tonight. A good night's rest will help you to continue on your journey," said the farmer.

Neither the farmer nor his wife cared whether or not the angels were poor women from the village. They just saw two tired, weary people, who needed help.

"But where will you sleep?" the older angel asked the farmer.

"Don't worry about us. We'll make a pallet on the floor in the room with our children. You are the ones who have been traveling up that dusty road and are in need of a good night's sleep. We feel blessed by your presence. We very seldom get any visitors," said the farmer.

So, the angels slept in the farmer's bed, while the farmer and his wife slept on the cold floor with a thin blanket and no pillow.

When the sun rose the next morning, the angels found the farmer and his wife in tears. Their only cow, whose milk had been their only source of income, lay dead in the field.

The younger angel was infuriated.

"How could you let this happen? The first family had everything, but were not nice people, yet you helped them by patching up the hole in the wall in their basement. This farmer and his wife had little, but were willing to share what they had, yet you took away their only source of income. You let their only cow die!" the younger angel complained.

The older angel looked at the younger angel and smiled.

"When we stayed in the basement of the mansion of the first family, I noticed there was gold buried in a hole in the wall and it had been there for years. The family was not aware of the gold. Since the owners were so obsessed with greed and unwilling to share their good fortune with others, I sealed the hole so they will never find the gold. Then, last night, as we slept in the farmer's bed, an Angel of Death came for the farmer's wife. I gave him the cow instead. When the farmer digs a hole to bury the cow, he will discover a bag of gold buried in his field. Things aren't always as they seem," replied the older angel.

The Price of a Miracle

Tess was seven years old and much smarter than her years. She had stood in the doorway of the living room of her home and listened to a conversation between her parents. After she had heard about the crisis her family was facing, she went to her bedroom and pulled a glass jelly jar from its hiding place in the closet. Tess dumped the change out on the floor and counted it carefully, three times. The total had to be exactly perfect. No chance for mistakes. Carefully placing the coins back into the jar and twisting on the cap, she took her coat and scarf from the door, put on her mittens to shield her hands from the cold weather, slipped out the back door and made her way six blocks to Rexall's Drug Store with the big red Indian Chief sign above the door.

Tess went inside the store to find Mr. Covington, the pharmacist, standing at the counter talking to a man Tess thought was a customer. She waited patiently for the pharmacist to give her some attention, but he was too busy with the conversation. Mr. Covington appeared to be really enjoying the conversation with the customer, a well-dressed man who looked a bit older than Mr. Covington.

Tess twisted her feet to make a scuffing noise. Mr. Covington ignored her and continued talking to the well-dressed man. She cleared her throat with the most disgusting sound she could muster. No good; he still ignored her. Finally, she took a quarter from her jar and banged it on the glass counter. That did it!

"And what do you want?" the pharmacist asked Tess, apparently annoyed by her interruption. "I'm talking to my brother from Chicago whom I haven't seen in ages," he said without waiting for a reply to his question.

"Well, I want to talk to you about my brother," Tess answered back in the same annoyed tone. "He's really sick... and I want to buy a miracle."

"I beg your pardon?" said the pharmacist.

"His name is Andrew, he's four years old, and he has something bad growing inside his head. My daddy says only a miracle can save him now. So how much does a miracle cost?"

"We don't sell miracles here, little girl. I'm sorry but I can't help you," the pharmacist said, softening a little.

"Listen, I have the money to pay for it. If it isn't enough, I will get the rest. Just tell me how much it costs."

The well-dressed man stooped down to match the eye level of Tess.

"What kind of a miracle does your brother need?" asked the stranger.

"I don't know," Tess replied, her eyes welling up with tears. "I just know he's really sick and Mommy says he needs an operation. But my daddy can't pay for it. So, I want to use my money to pay for it."

"How much money do you have?" asked the man from Chicago.

Tess answered in a little more than a whisper, "One dollar and eleven cents. It's all the money I have, but I can get some more if I need to. I'll get a job."

The well-dressed man smiled at the thought of the tiny little girl talking about getting a job. "Well, what a coincidence! A dollar and eleven cents... That's the exact price of a miracle for little brothers."

He took her money in one hand and with the other hand he grasped her mitten and said, "Take me to where you live. I want to see your brother and meet your parents. Let's see if I have the miracle you need."

The well-dressed man went with Tess to her home and spoke with her parents. He convinced them to schedule an appointment for him to examine their son. Upon examination, he scheduled a day to perform an operation.

The well-dressed man was a surgeon, specializing in neurosurgery. The operation was completed free of charge, and it wasn't long before Andrew was home again and doing well.

One day, Tess's mom and dad were happily talking about the chain of events that had saved their son's life.

Tess's mom whispered to her husband, "That surgery was a real miracle. I wonder how much it would have cost."

Tess overheard and smiled to herself. She knew exactly how much a miracle cost... One dollar and eleven cents.

Jesus's File System

Brian Moore was finishing his last semester in his creative writing class. Soon, he would be graduating with a Bachelor's Degree in theology. During his younger years he had lived life in the fast lane, drinking, doing drugs, and hanging out with people who were gang members. So, when he told his family that he wanted to become a minister, they were pleasantly surprised. One of his last class assignments was to write an essay about how he wanted to be remembered when his work on Earth was through. For several weeks, he had mulled over what he wanted to write about. He finally settled on a subject. He thought about an earlier conversation he had with his best friend, Doug, about forgiveness and letting go of the past.

"We often have disagreements with people and we get so filled with anger that we don't speak to each other again. We remember the wrong that someone did to us and we hold a grudge, not realizing that life is too short to hold malice in our hearts. I was thinking one night, what if God kept a tickler file on us to record all of the things we have done which He didn't approve?" said Brian. "There are things in my past that I don't want to remember, things I'm not proud about. So, I'm glad that God forgives our transgressions."

Brian wrote his essay and put it in his locker. Later at dinner, his father asked Brian how his essay was coming?

"I finished it but I'm not ready to turn it in right now. We still have a week before the final due date," said Brian. "But it's the best thing I ever wrote!"

It was also the last thing he ever wrote. Brian died the following day, May 27, 1997, the day after Memorial Day. He was driving home from a friend's house when his car went off the road and struck a utility pole. He emerged from the wreck unharmed but stepped on a downed power line and was electrocuted.

After Brian's funeral, his parents had forgotten about his essay when a cousin found it while cleaning out Brian's school locker. Brian had been dead only days, and his parents desperately wanted every piece of his life near them—notes from classmates, teachers, his homework, anything and everything that reminded them of their son's life on Earth.

When they read Brian's essay it was about encountering Jesus in a file room full of cards that detailed every moment of Brian's life. But it was only after Brian's death that Beth and Bruce Moore realized that their son had described his view of Heaven in the last essay he had written.

"It makes such an impact that people want to share it. You feel like you are there," Mr. Moore said.

Brian's mother framed a copy of Brian's essay and hung it among the family portraits in their living room. One day they were entertaining friends in their home and were discussing their son.

"I think God used Brian to make a point. I think we were meant to find it and make something out of it," Mrs. Moore said.

She and her husband wanted to share their son's vision of life after death.

"I'm happy for Brian. I know he's in Heaven. I know I'll see him again."

Brian's Essay: The Room

In that place between wakefulness and dreams, I found myself in a room where there were no distinguishing features except for one wall that was covered with small index card files. They were like the ones in libraries that list titles by author or subject in alphabetical order. But these files, which stretched from floor to ceiling and were seemingly endless in either direction, had very different headings. As I drew near the wall of files, the first to catch my attention was one that read "Girls I have liked."

I opened it and began flipping through the cards. I quickly shut it, shocked to realize that I recognized the names written on each one. And then without being told, I knew exactly where I was. This room with its small files was a crude catalog system of my life. Here were written the actions of my every moment, big and small, in stark detail that my memory couldn't match. A sense of wonder and curiosity, coupled with horror, stirred within me as I began randomly opening files and exploring their content. Some brought joy and sweet memories and others a sense of shame and regret so intense that I would look over my shoulder to see if anyone was watching.

A file named "Friends" was next to one marked "Friends I have betrayed." The titles ranged from the mundane to the outright weird: "Books I Have Read," "Lies I Have Told," "Comfort I Have Given," "Jokes I Have Laughed At." Some were almost hilarious in their exactness: "Things I've Yelled at My Brothers." Others I couldn't laugh at: "Things I Have Done in My Anger," "Things I Have Muttered Under My Breath at My Parents." I never ceased to be surprised by the contents.

Often, in the files there would be many more cards than I expected. Sometimes fewer than I hoped. I was overwhelmed by the sheer volume of the life I had lived.

Could it be possible that I had the time in my years to fill each of these thousands or even millions of cards? But each card confirmed this truth. Each one was written in my own handwriting and signed with my signature.

When I pulled out the file marked "TV Shows I Have Watched," I realized the files grew to contain their contents. The cards were packed tightly and yet after two or three yards, I was still looking to find the end of the file. I shut it, shamed, not so much by the low quality of shows but more by the huge length of time I knew that file represented.

When I came to a file marked "Lustful Thoughts," I felt a chill run through my body. I pulled the file out only an inch, not willing to test its size, and drew out a card. I shuddered at its detailed content.

I felt sick to think that such a moment had been recorded. An almost animal rage broke in me. One thought dominated my mind: "No one must ever see these cards! No one must ever see this room! I have to destroy them!" With insane frenzy, I yanked the file out. Its size didn't matter now. I had to empty it and burn the cards. But as I grasped it and began pounding it on the floor, I could not dislodge a single card. I became desperate and pulled out a card, only to find it was as strong as steel when I tried to tear it.

Defeated and utterly helpless, I returned the file to its slot. Leaning my forehead against the wall, I let out a long, self-pitying sigh. And then I saw it. The title of the file was "People I Have Shared the Gospel With." The handle was brighter than those around it, newer, almost unused. I pulled on its handle and a small box not more than three inches long fell into my hands. I could count the cards it contained on one hand.

And then the tears came. I began to weep with sobs so deep that it hurt. The pain started in my stomach and shook through me. I fell on my knees and cried. I cried out of shame, from the overwhelming shame of it all. The rows of file shelves swirled in my tear-filled eyes. No one could ever,

ever know of this room. I knew I had to lock it up and hide the key. But then as I pushed away the tears, I saw Him.

No, please, not Him. Not here. Oh, anyone but Jesus. I watched helplessly as He began to open the files and read the cards. I couldn't bear to watch His response. And in the moments when I could bring myself to look at His face, I saw a sorrow deeper than my own.

He seemed to intuitively go to the worst boxes. Why did He have to read every one? Finally, He turned and looked at me from across the room. He looked at me with pity in His eyes. But this was a pity that didn't anger me. I dropped my head, covered my face with my hands and began to weep. He walked over and put His arm around me. He could have said so many things. But He didn't say a word. He just wept with me.

Then He got up and walked back to the wall of files. Starting at one end of the room, He took out a file and, one by one, began to sign His name over mine on each card.

"No!" I shouted, rushing to Him. All I could find to say was "No, no!"

I pulled the cards from His hands.

His name should not be on these cards. But there it was, written in red so rich, so dark, so alive. The name of Jesus covered mine. It was written with His blood. He gently took the cards back from me. He smiled a sad smile and continued signing each card. I don't think I'll ever understand how He did it so quickly, but in a few moments, He closed the last file and walked to my side.

He placed His hand on my shoulder.

"It is finished. Come, my child, and go with me," He said in a gentle voice.

I stood up, and He led me out of the room. There was no lock on the door. There were still cards to be written.

What will your cards say? Will you be proud of your cards in the file? Isn't it wonderful that God in His infinite mercy is a forgiving God? Where would we be if He ruled with justice rather than mercy?

Nobody Invited Nathan

His name was Nathan and he was a blacksmith, and a most wretchedly wicked, mean, obnoxious man. He hated everything that was good, and loved everything that was bad and evil. He would never set foot inside a church but you couldn't keep him away from dance halls and gambling joints.

Nathan seemed to deliberately make himself an irritation to all who believed in God. Nathan's wife, Rosa, was a Christian woman, who went to church every Sunday, and to Bible study on Wednesday nights. No one could understand how two people as mismatched as Nathan and Rosa could stay together. They didn't have any children. They just seemed to take care of each other. Rosa did the best she could in the patience and kingdom of Jesus. However, the good people of Williamsburg, where Nathan and Rosa lived, had given up on Nathan as being beyond moral recovery, and so indeed he seemed.

A few miles back in the country from the blacksmith's town lived an old couple whom everyone referred to as Father and Mother Jenkins. They were close to ninety years of age. Theirs had been lives of conscious acceptance with God and of patient unremitting devotedness to Him. Both of them were waiting without sorrow and without fear for the promised homecoming. Very early one morning, Father Jenkins awoke terribly agitated and began to call his wife.

"Get up, wife! Get up!"

"Why, old man? What's the matter?"

"I can't tell you now what's the matter; I don't have time. I must start a fire in the kitchen. I want you to get breakfast ready as soon as you can. I've got to go into town this morning."

"You're going into town?" she exclaimed. "You must be out of your head. You can't go to town. You don't have any way of getting there and I know you can't walk that far."

Father Jenkins persisted. "Don't tell me what I can't do. I tell you; I've got to go into town. I had a dream last night, and, well, after I make the fire, I'll tell you about it."

Mother Jenkins saw how agitated her husband was and thought it best not to push the conversation any more. She proceeded to prepare their breakfast. When they finished eating, Father Jenkins started for town. It was a long and weary way for an old man to walk, but some strange strength had overtaken him and without stopping to rest he kept walking, as if he were possessed.

Finally, he reached the village. He trudged through the narrow main street, then into the narrow cross street and went into the shop of Nathan the blacksmith. People in the little town called him "Devil Nathan."

Father Jenkins walked into the shop and Devil Nathan looked at him and exclaimed in great amazement.

"Father Jenkins! What are you doing here so early in the morning?"

Father Jenkins answered, "That's just what I've come to tell you. Let's sit down and talk. I'm tired from that long walk to get here."

When they were seated, Father Jenkins started talking.

"Nathan, I had a strange dream last night, and I've come to tell you about it. I dreamed that the hour I have thought about so much and tried to be ready when it came, had come. I dreamed that it was my time to die. I dreamed that I went to Heaven, and it was just as wonderful and beautiful as I thought it would be. I wasn't the least bit afraid. My room was filled with angels. They all loved me and I loved them. It was as if they all knew me. I didn't feel like a stranger. Two of them held me under each arm and we began to fly. We flew beyond the hills and beyond the clouds. We flew through the starry skies and as we flew, the angels sang. Oh, how they sang! I never heard such beautiful music in my life. Then one of them said: 'Look yonder, now; there's Heaven!'

"Oh, Nathan, I can't tell you how I felt when I was in sight of Heaven; nor can I tell you what I saw when I looked. I don't believe anyone could describe it. It was so peaceful, so beautiful, so pure, and so glorious! As we drew nearer, I saw the gates swinging open, and with even faster wings than we had come we swept through the gates and into the city. I received such a welcome from everybody! Every hill was filled with the fragrance of the flowers that grew there. In the music of every harp, in the song of every tongue, in the grasp of every hand, there was gladness everywhere, because I had come. They treated me like I was somebody, when I was only a poor man saved by Jesus's blood.

"I saw all my children there—not one of them lost. My boy who died in that car accident last year was there. He's the one you used to play with so much when you went to school together. Your mother and father were there. After a time—I don't know how long it was—I saw the same angels who had brought me earlier bring another; and it was my dear, sweet wife. I loved her more than ever when they brought her to me there. She was more beautiful than the day we married. She and I sat under the Tree of Life together, then we walked by the river that flows from the throne of God. We were so happy! I saw angels bringing in others—others that I love and you love. And so, the years of eternity rolled.

"Then, Nathan, all at once it came to me that I hadn't seen you anywhere. I set out to look for you. I went into every street. I asked everybody where you were, but no one could find a trace of you. I was distressed more than I could ever say. Then I went to the Lord, my precious Savior, and asked Him where you were. A sad look came over His face when I mentioned your name. I wish you could have seen how sorry He was when He told me that you hadn't come. 'He hasn't come? Why didn't Nathan come?' I asked. The Lord wept.

Then He spoke and His voice was the sweetest sound I have ever heard when he said, 'Nobody asked Nathan to come, nobody has invited him.'

"I fell at His feet and I washed them with my tears. I laid my cheeks upon them and cried: 'Blessed Lord! Just let me out of here for half an hour, and I'll go and ask Nathan to come. I'll give him a special invitation.'

"After I said that, I woke up. It was beginning to get light in the east, and I was glad that I was alive, so I could come and ask you to prepare yourself to go to Heaven. Now here I am; and I have told you my dream. Do you want to go to Heaven?"

Nathan stood as if he were petrified. He couldn't speak nor move. Father Jenkins got up to leave.

"Good-bye, Nathan, and remember you've got the invitation; remember you were asked to come."

Father Jenkins took his walking cane and started home. Nathan seemed to come to himself, and, as one recovering from a magician's charm, he set out to pursue the labors of the day. But everything went wrong—the bellows would not work right. The hammer would not strike right. The nails would not go in right. The horses would not stand right.

"Oh God, be merciful to me, a sinner!" cried Nathan.

He began to sob at last. He closed up the shop and went home. He told his wife of Father Jenkins's visit.

"Blessed be God!" she said. "We will send the horse and buggy and have Father Jenkins come over for dinner."

"Yes, for I intend to accept the invitation. I want him to pray to God to keep me true and steadfast to the end. I don't want to be missing in Heaven because no one asked me. The members of the church have asked me several times, and every time I refused to give God my heart. This Sunday, I will accept the invitation. I thank Father Jenkins for inviting me to come. When the roll is called in Heaven, I want to be there to answer when my name is called."

The next morning, Nathan received shocking news. Father Jenkins had passed away peacefully in his sleep. Instantly, Nathan knew that the dream Father Jenkins had was real, without a shadow of a doubt. And, as well as feeling devastated by this saintly man's death, he felt truly blessed and grateful to have had this warning, this invitation to Heaven, from him before he died. Already, Nathan was looking forward to their reunion in Heaven and lived the rest of his life as a devoted Christian, telling everyone he met this amazing tale.

What Goes Around, Comes Around

Drake almost didn't see, Leslie Walker, an old lady who was standing on the side of the road beside her car—a Mercedes. Even in the dim light of day, he could see she needed help. So, he pulled up in front of her car and got out. Drake's Pontiac was still sputtering when he approached her.

Leslie Walker, eyed Drake with discomfort. Even with the smile on his face, she was still apprehensive about the approaching stranger. No one had stopped to help her for the last hour or so. Was he going to hurt her? He didn't look safe; he looked poor and hungry.

Drake could see that she was frightened, standing alone out there in the cold. He knew how she felt. It was that chill which only fear can put in you.

"I'm here to help you, ma'am," said Drake, trying to ease the woman's fear. Why don't you wait in the car where it's warm? By the way, my name is Drake Anderson."

"Hello, young man. My name is Leslie Walker. Thank you for being so kind," as she got back into the warmth and safety of her car.

All she had was a flat tire, but for an old lady, that was bad enough. Drake crawled under the car looking for a place to put the jack, skinning his knuckles a time or two. Soon, he was able to change the tire, but he'd had to get dirty and his hands now hurt. As he was tightening up the lug nuts, Leslie Walker rolled down the window and began to talk to Drake. She told him that she was from St. Louis and was only passing through. She couldn't thank him enough for coming to her aid. Drake smiled as he closed her car trunk.

Leslie asked how much she owed him. Any amount would have been all right with her. She had earlier imagined the awful things that could have happened had he not stopped to help her.

Drake never thought about being paid. This was not a job to him. This was helping someone in need, and God knows there were plenty people who had come to his aid in the past. He had lived his whole life that way, and it never occurred to him to act any other way. Drake told her that if she really wanted to pay him back, the next time she saw someone who needed help, she could give that person the assistance they needed. After a pause, he added, "And think of me."

Drake waited until she started her car and drove off. It had been a cold and depressing day, but he felt good as he headed for home, disappearing into the twilight.

A few miles down the road Leslie saw a small café. She went in to grab a bite to eat, and take the chill off before she made the last leg of her trip home. It was a dingy-looking restaurant. Outside were two old gas pumps. The whole scene was unfamiliar to her.

The waitress had a sweet smile, one that even being on her feet for the whole day couldn't erase. Leslie noticed the waitress was pregnant, but she never let the strain and aches change her attitude. Leslie wondered how someone who looked so weary and appeared to have so little could be so pleasant to a stranger.

Then she remembered Drake. After Leslie finished her meal, she paid with a hundred-dollar bill. The waitress quickly went to get change, but Leslie had slipped out the door. She was gone by the time the waitress came back with the change.

The waitress wondered where the lady had gone. Then the waitress noticed something written on the napkin laying by the old lady's empty plate. There were tears in her eyes when she read what the lady wrote:

"You don't owe me anything. I have been there too. Somebody once helped me out, the way I'm helping you. If you really want to pay me back, here is what you do: Do not let this chain of love end with you."

Under the napkin were four more $100 bills. There were tables to clear, sugar bowls to fill, and people to serve, but the waitress made it through another day. That night when she got home from work and climbed into bed, she was thinking about the money and what the lady had written. How could the lady have known how much she and her husband needed the cash? With the baby due next month, it was going to be hard...

She knew how worried her husband was, and as he lay sleeping next to her, she gave him a soft kiss and whispered soft and low in his ear:

"Everything's going to be all right. I love you, Drake Anderson."

You Reap What You Sow

A successful Christian business man was growing old and knew it was time to choose a successor to take over his prosperous multi-million-dollar corporation. Instead of choosing one of his directors or one of his children, he decided to do something different. He called together all the young executives in his company.

"It is time for me to step down as director of this corporation and choose the next CEO. I have decided to choose one of you," he said to the young executives.

The young executives were shocked, but their boss continued, "I am going to give each of you a packet of three geranium seeds today; they are my favorite flowers. I want you to plant the seeds, water them, and come back here one year from today with what you have grown from the seeds I have given you. I will then judge the plants that you bring and the one I choose will be the next CEO."

Among the people there that day to receive the seeds was a man named Troy. He went home excitedly and told his wife the story behind the seeds. She helped him get a pot, soil and compost and he planted the seeds. Every day, he watered them and watched to see if they had grown. After about three weeks, some of the other executives began to talk about their seeds and the plants that were beginning to grow. Troy kept checking his seeds, but nothing ever grew. Three weeks, four weeks, five weeks went by, and still nothing. By then, others were talking about their plants and bragging about how beautifully they were growing. But Troy didn't have any plants to brag about and he felt like a failure.

Six months went by—and still there was nothing in Troy's pot, no signs of any growth. He thought he had killed his seeds. Everyone else had tall plants and bragged about their growth, but he had nothing. However, Troy didn't say anything to his colleagues. He was too embarrassed. He just kept watering and fertilizing the soil—he very much wanted his seeds to grow. He moved the pot from the direct sun into the indirect sun, then into the shade; he tried different fertilizers, and still nothing happened. Meanwhile, his colleagues continued to brag about how their plants were growing. They even exchanged formulas of different fertilizers.

Finally, a year went by and all the young executives of the company brought their plants to the CEO for inspection. Troy told his wife that he wasn't going to take an empty pot to the meeting and be embarrassed. But she convinced him to be honest and truthful with the CEO about the result of this effort. Troy felt sick in his stomach. It was going to be the most embarrassing moment of his life but he knew his wife was right.

He took his empty pot to the board room, dreading each step that took him closer to the ridicule of his colleagues. When he arrived in the board room, he was amazed at the beautiful plants grown by the other executives. They were all in different colors and sizes. The young executives proudly displayed their plants. They sat them on the table, any place where their plants could be seen. Troy put his empty pot on the floor trying to hide it under the conference table. Many of Troy's colleagues laughed at his empty pot, and a few even expressed their sympathy to him.

When the CEO arrived, he surveyed the room and greeted his young executives. Troy tried to hide in the back, too embarrassed to look at the CEO, afraid of being labeled a failure.

"My, what great flowers you have grown!" the CEO said to the young executives.

This caused them to beam with pride. Some of them lovingly stroked the leaves of their plants.

"Today, one of you will be appointed the next CEO to run this corporation!"

The CEO looked around the room at the beaming smiles on the faces of the young executives. Then, he spotted Troy at the back of the room. He seemed to be trying hard not to be noticed. He wasn't standing beside his prize plant as were the other executives.

When Troy saw the CEO looking at him he lowered his head, wishing he could just disappear. The CEO ordered Troy to come to the front of the room and to bring his pot with him. Troy was terrified; he thought, *The CEO knows I'm a failure! Maybe he will fire me on the spot!*

As Troy walked slowly to the front of the room, dreading each step, walking amongst his colleagues, he heard their snickering and saw the looks of pity on some of their faces. When Troy got to the front of the room the CEO asked him what happened to his seeds. Troy explained in all honesty how he had planted the seeds, watered them, placed the pot with the seeds in the sunlight, and had even used fertilizer on them but they still would not grow.

The CEO asked everyone to sit down except Troy. He looked at Troy, turned to face the young executives, pointed at Troy and said, "Troy is your next Chief Executive!"

Troy couldn't believe what he was hearing and neither could the young executives.

"Troy couldn't even grow his seeds. How could he be the new CEO?" someone asked.

Then the CEO said, "One year ago today, I gave each of you a packet of seeds. I instructed you to take the seeds home, plant them, water them, and that we'll meet again one year later so that you can show me the results of how you took care of your seeds. Today is the day you were to show me how you had taken care of your seeds. But what you didn't know is that I gave each of you boiled seeds; they were dead, so it was not possible for them to grow. All of you, except Troy, have brought me flowers, beautiful healthy plants. When you found that your seeds would not grow, you replaced the seeds I gave you with other ones. Troy was the only one with the courage and honesty to bring me a pot with my seeds in it. He is the only one who followed my instructions to the letter and was brave enough to face me when my instructions did not yield the desired results. Therefore, he is the person I want to lead this corporation."

The moral of this story is: never allow your urge to win to define your character. Never allow your competitive nature to lead you onto a path of deceit and dishonesty. Integrity, honesty, truthfulness and courage are some of the characteristics of a leader. Let your word be your bond and lead by example.

Finding God

A university professor once wrote an article to be published in the university's newsletter about a student in his Theology of Faith class named Davon. The professor wanted the entire university to learn about what he thought was an amazing young man. Here follows the contents of his article:

Some years ago, I stood watching my university students file into the classroom for the first session of the Theology of Faith class. That was the day I first saw Davon. He was combing his long flaxen hair, which hung six inches below his shoulders. It was the first time I had ever seen a boy with hair that long. I guess it was just coming into fashion then for men to wear their hair long like women. I know in my mind that it isn't what's *on* the head that counts, but what's *in* the head that characterizes a person. But, on that day, I was unprepared for what was to happen and my emotions flipped. I immediately filed Davon in my mind under "S" for strange... Very strange. Davon turned out to be the atheist in residence in my Theology of Faith course. He constantly objected to, smirked at, or whined about the possibility of an unconditionally loving Father/God. He did not believe that God existed.

Davon and I remained in each other's company in relative peace for one semester, although I admit he was, at times, a serious pain in the butt. When he came to me at the end of the course to turn in his final exam, he looked at me and smirked.

"Do you think I'll ever find God?" he asked in a cynical tone.

I decided to respond with a little shock therapy. "No!" I said very emphatically.

"Why not?" Davon responded in a cynical tone. "I thought that was the product you were pushing," he added as he began to walk out of the classroom.

I let him get to five steps from the classroom door and then I called out to him.

"Davon! I don't think you'll ever find Him, but I am absolutely certain that He will find you!"

"Whatever," he said nonchalantly and waved me off.

"He shrugged his shoulders and left my class and my life. I felt slightly disappointed at the thought that he had missed the meaning of my clever line, 'He will find you!' At least, I thought it was clever. A few years later, I heard that Davon had graduated, and I was duly grateful. However, four months after I learned he had graduated, a sad report came. I heard that Davon had terminal cancer.

Before I could search him out, he came to see me. When he walked into my office, his body was very badly wasted and his long hair had all fallen out as a result of chemotherapy. But his eyes were bright and his voice was firm, for the first time, I believe.

"Davon, I've thought about you so often; I hear you are sick," I blurted out.

"Oh, yes, very sick. I have cancer in both lungs. It's a matter of weeks before I'll be gone."

I didn't know what to say, or how to say it. I decided to be honest and ask the questions I really wanted to know the answers to. Davon had been that kind of student, straightforward and to the point. He was a no-nonsense type of student. I was sure he wouldn't mind the questions I wanted to ask.

"Can you talk about it, Davon?"

"Sure, what would you like to know?"

"What's it like to be only twenty-four years old and dying?"

Without hesitating, he responded, "Well, it could be worse."

I thought that was an odd answer, but I didn't want to show my confusion. I relaxed my voice before I spoke again. "What do you mean it could be worse? Like, how?"

"Well, like being fifty and having no values or ideals, or thinking that booze, seducing women, and making money are the real biggies in life."

I began to look through my mental file cabinet under "S" where I had filed Davon as strange. By then, it seemed to me as though everybody I had ever tried to reject by classification, God had sent back into my life to educate me.

Davon looked at me and smiled with a strange expression on his face. I wondered if he knew the significance of my mental box.

Then, still smiling, he spoke. "What I really came to see you about is something you said to me on the last day of class."

He remembered! I thought. I was both impressed and excited to hear this.

He continued, "I asked you if you thought I would ever find God and you said, 'No!' which surprised me. Then you said, 'But He will find you.' I thought about that a lot, even though my search for God was hardly intense at the time."

My clever line. He thought about that a lot! Yeah, I did get through to him, albeit just a little... I thought. I was pleased that, at least, all my effort with him hadn't been in vain.

"But when the doctors removed a lump from my groin and told me that it was malignant, that's when I got serious about locating God," he said. "When the malignancy spread into my vital organs, I really began banging bloody fists against the bronze doors of Heaven. But God did not come out. In fact, nothing happened. Professor, did you ever try anything for a long time with great effort and with no success? Have you ever got psychologically fed up with trying something, and then just quit? Well, one day, I woke up, and instead of throwing a few more futile appeals over that high brick wall to a God who may be or may not be there, I just quit. I decided that I didn't really care about God, about an afterlife, or anything like that. I decided to spend what little time I had left doing something more profitable. I thought about you and your class and I remembered something else you had said: 'The essential sadness is to go through life without loving. But it would be almost equally sad to go through life and leave this world without ever telling those you love that you love them.'

"So, I began with the hardest one... my dad. He was sitting in our living room in his favorite chair reading the newspaper when I approached him. I said to him, 'Dad?' and, without lowering the newspaper, he asked, 'Yes, what?'

"So, I said, 'Dad, I would like to talk with you.'

"'Well, talk!' he said.

"'I mean, it's really important.'

"He slowly lowered the newspaper about three inches from his face and said, 'What is it?'

"'Dad, I love you. I just wanted you to know that,' I said to him."

Davon smiled at me when he said these words with obvious satisfaction, as though he felt a warm and secret joy flowing inside of him.

"The newspaper fluttered to the floor. Then my father did two things I could never remember him ever doing before. He cried and he hugged me. My father and I talked all night, even though he had to go to work the next morning. It felt good to be close to my father, to see his tears, to feel his hug, to hear him say that he loved me too.

"It was easier with my mother and little brother. When I told them I loved them, they cried with me, too. We hugged each other, and started saying really nice things to each other. We shared the things we had been keeping secret for so many years. I was only sorry about one thing: that I had waited so long to say those things, or to really find out how they felt. Here I was, just beginning to open up to all the people I had actually been close to, and I wouldn't have much time left to enjoy that feeling of being loved and giving love.

"Then, one day, I turned around and God was there, in the love of my family, in the breeze of the fresh air, in the sunshine I felt on my face. I felt as if I were a new person. He didn't come to me when I pleaded with Him. I guess I was like an animal trainer holding out a hoop, saying, 'C'mon, jump through. C'mon, I'll give you three days, three weeks.' Apparently, God does things in His own way and at His own hour. But the important thing is that He was there. He found me! You were right. He found me even after I had stopped looking for Him."

I practically gasped.

"Davon, I think you're saying something very important and much more universal than you realize. To me, at least, you are saying that the surest way to find God is not to make Him a private possession, a problem solver, or an instant consolation in time of need, but rather by opening to love. You know, the Apostle John said that. He said: 'God is love, and anyone who lives in love is living with God and God is living in him.'

"Davon, could I ask you a favor?"

"Of course, Professor, you can ask me anything."

"You know, when you were in my class you were a real pain. But you can make it all up to me now. Will you come into my present Theology of Faith class and tell my students what you have just told me? If I told them the same thing it wouldn't be half as powerful as it would be if you were to tell it."

Davon looked surprised.

"Pooh. I was ready for you, but I don't know if I'm ready for your class."

"Think about it, Davon, and let me know. If and when you are ready, give me a call."

A few days later, Davon called and said he was ready to talk to my class. He said that he wanted to do it for God and for me. So, we scheduled a date. However, he never made it. He had another appointment, far more important than the one with me and my class. He had an appointment with God. Of course, his life was not really ended by his death, only changed. He made the great step from faith into vision. He found a life far more beautiful than the eye of Man has ever seen, or the ear of Man has ever heard, or the mind of Man has ever imagined. Before he died, we talked one last time. He had been admitted to the hospital and I went to visit him. It was obvious that it was only a matter of time before he died. He was failing fast.

"I'm not going to make it to your class," he said as he lay in the hospital bed.

"I know, Davon," I said, trying hard not to let him see me cry.

"Will you tell them for me? Will you ... tell the whole world for me that God is real?"

"I will, Davon. I'll tell them. I'll do my best."

So, to all of you who have been kind enough to read this simple story about God's love, thank you for listening. And to you, Davon, somewhere in the sunlit, vibrant hills of Heaven—I told them, Davon, as best I could.

With thanks,

Rev. John Powell
Professor, Loyola University, Chicago

Beauty in Aging

Someone asked me one day how it felt getting old. Did I worry about dying? Was I afraid of death? Instead of replying to these questions, I told them the following story:

One day, a rich traveler was driving through the South looking at the land, trying to decide where he should build the country home he had dreamed of building for years. He just couldn't find the right materials to use. In his mind he knew what he wanted but he hadn't yet found it.

He drove through the country on this spring day, enjoying the breeze far away from the hustle and fast-paced living of the city up north where he lived. He passed many dilapidated shacks that time seemed to have forgotten. Those shacks once were the homes of families that had either died or moved away and left the shells of a past life behind.

As he drove, he imagined what the families who once lived in the dilapidated shacks were like. Who were they? Where had they gone? What did their children do with their lives? Were they doctors, teachers, scientists? It was apparent that years of neglect and adverse weather had taken their toll on what were once beautiful structures. However, although worn, the wood of some of those barns was still beautiful. Only years of standing in the weather, battling the storms and the scorching sun, could have produced such beautiful barn wood.

As the traveler turned onto a back road where time seemed to stand still, off from the main highway, hidden in tall grass and trees, he saw an old weather-beaten barn. He thought the wood of the barn was exactly what he was looking for to put into his dream country house. A little way up a path stood a huge, white farmhouse where he presumed the owners of the worn barn lived.

The traveler decided to stop and make an offer to purchase the barn. He drove up to the big white house and knocked on the door. The farmer answered and the traveler explained that he wanted to buy the old barn that sat by the highway and proceeded to explain how beautiful he thought it was. He said it was exactly what he had been looking for and wanted to know how much he would take for it. The farmer thought the traveler was crazy for wanting to purchase a worthless barn.

The farmer could tell by the traveler's clothes, his car, his hands, and the way he spoke that he was a city type. The traveler said he was driving by and saw that beautiful barn sitting out in the tall grass and wanted to know if it was for sale. The farmer looked at the traveler with a puzzled look on his face. He grinned and said:

"You sure got a pretty unusual idea of what beauty is. Sure, that old barn was a handsome building in its day. But there have been a lot of winters with heavy snow, ice and howling winds. The scorching sun of the past summers done beat down on that old barn 'till all the paint is gone and the wood done turned to silver gray. Now that old building tilts to one side and it looks kind of tired. Yet, you call it beautiful."

"To me, it's beautiful," said the traveler. "It's made of beautiful, natural pieces of wood weathered by nature. You can't manufacture that. It comes naturally."

The farmer walked with the traveler out into the field to get a better look at the old barn. They both quietly stood gazing at it, each seeing it differently. The farmer saw it as a worthless piece of junk that wasn't worth spending money to have it removed, and the traveler saw it as a thing of beauty that had many more years of beautifying its surroundings. The traveler said he planned to use the wood of the barn to line the walls of his den in a new country home he was building down the road.

"You can't get paint that beautiful. Only years of standing in the weather, against the storms and scorching sun, can produce beautiful wood like that," said the traveler.

The farmer accepted the traveler's offer and sold him the barn. They hauled away the wood from the old barn and used it to beautify the inside of the rich traveler's house.

As we age, we are a lot like that old barn. Someday, we will be hauled off to Heaven to take on whatever chores the Good Lord has for us on the Great Sky Ranch. And I suspect we'll be more beautiful after all the hardship we've been through here on Earth, and just maybe we'll even add a bit of beauty to our Father's house.

It's on the inside that the beauty of age and wisdom and experiences shine to glow on the outside for the world to see and admire. Sure, our hair turns gray, our eyesight turns dim, and as we age, we "tilt to one side" a bit more than we did when we were young and full of energy. But the Good Lord knows what He's doing. And as the years pass, He's busy using the hard weather of our lives, the dry spells and the stormy seasons, to do a job of beautifying our souls in a way that nothing else can.

And to think how often folks complain because the weather of life is hard and they want it easy... They don't realize they are still standing regardless of how hard life has been and not only are they still standing, but they have also acquired an inner beauty because of the harsh storms of life they have weathered.

The Urge to Pray

Have you ever felt the urge to pray for someone and then just put the thought out of your mind and said, "I'll pray for them later?" Or has anyone ever called you and said, "I need you to pray for me?"

If that ever happens to you, don't put it off for a later time; pray at that moment. It may be God talking to you telling you to help someone in trouble, someone standing in the need of prayer. The following story better explains the importance of praying when you get the urge. It is told by a missionary who was also a medical doctor on furlough while visiting his home church in Michigan. In the story, he is addressing the congregation:

"While I was a doctor serving at a small field hospital in Africa, every two weeks, I traveled by bicycle through the jungle to a nearby city for supplies. This was a journey of two days and required me to camp overnight in the jungle at the halfway point.

On one of those journeys, I arrived in the city where I planned to collect money from a bank, purchase medicine and supplies, and then begin my two-day journey back to the field hospital. Upon arrival in the city, I observed two men fighting, one of whom had been seriously injured. I treated his injuries and, at the same time, I talked to him about the Lord. I then traveled two days back to the hospital, camping overnight, and arrived home without incident.

"Two weeks later, I repeated my journey. Upon arriving in the city, I was approached by the young man I had treated two weeks prior. He told me that he and other men in the village who were thieves and unsavory characters knew that I carried money and medicines.

"He said, 'Some of my buddies, and the man I was fighting with, whom you saw the last time you came into the city and treated my wounds, followed you into the jungle on your way home, knowing you would camp overnight. They planned to kill you and take your money and the drugs you were taking back to the hospital. But as they were about to move into your camp, they saw that you were surrounded by twenty-six armed guards. Where did those guards come from? You didn't bring them with you into the city. Were they waiting for you in the jungle?'

"At that, I laughed and said they were teasing him because I was certainly all alone in that jungle campsite. I had traveled from the hospital to the city alone. However, the young man pressed the point.

"He said, 'No sir, all of my buddies saw the armed guards and came running back from the jungle in fear. My buddies counted them. It was because of those guards that the men were afraid and did not harm you.'

"Still, I laughed and dismissed the story thinking the men had imagined they saw twenty-six guards and were probably drunk."

The missionary relayed this story while standing before the congregation in his home church in Michigan, as previously mentioned. At this point in his testimony, one of the men in the congregation jumped to his feet and interrupted the missionary to ask if he could identify the exact day this happened.

The missionary told the congregation the date, and the man who had interrupted him said, "The night of your incident in Africa, it was morning here and I was playing golf. I was about to putt when I felt the urge to pray for you. In fact, the urging of the Lord was so strong I called some men in this church to meet with me here in the sanctuary to pray for you. All those men who met with me here in the sanctuary on that day please stand up."

The men who had met together to pray that day stood up. The missionary wasn't concerned with who they were; he was too busy counting *how many* they were. They were twenty-six...

Barbara A. Robinson

This story is an incredible example of how the Spirit of the Lord moves on behalf of those who love Him. If you ever hear such prodding, go along with it. Nothing is ever hurt by prayer except the gates of Hell.

A Mother's Love

For those who are fortunate enough to still be blessed by having their mother around, still living, this is a beautiful story. For those who aren't, it is even more beautiful. I hope you enjoy the journey on which this story takes you. I certainly did! This beautiful story was sent to me by Charles Taylor, a beautiful soul who experienced some personal health challenges and could not attend events as often as he once used to, but he still could write wonderful stories.

One beautiful day in Heaven, as God walked around His Kingdom, He saw an angel sitting alone looking sad. He walked to where she was sitting and put His arms around her.

"Why are you so sad on a beautiful day like this, my child?" He asked.

"Father, Gabriel just informed me that it's my turn to go to Earth and I'm afraid. I don't want to leave my heavenly home where there is so much peace and love. I've heard stories about the turmoil and violence on Earth. So many people are hurting each other, and there is so much mistrust, even between family members and friends. Here, we trust each other and each day is filled with peace and love, but on Earth there is a lack of hope and there doesn't appear to be any peace. Father, You can override Gabriel's decision to send me to Earth; please help me."

God looked into the sad eyes of the angel.

"Gabriel made his decision after much discussion with Me. I agree with his decision. When you go to Earth, you will bring happiness to a young couple who lost their only son in an accident when he drowned in a neighbor's backyard swimming pool. He was only four years old and the family has been grieving for a long time. You will be their bundle of joy to help them heal emotionally. You will not stop them from hurting but you can help lessen their pain. Going to

Earth is an important task for you. You will be helping many people who will not be able to have any more children; therefore, you will be a gift from Heaven to them."

"How can I, just one angel, be a gift from Heaven, Father?"

"Because you will grow up to be the mother of children who will contribute much to bringing peace to Mankind. Let me tell you a story about how your life on Earth will be. Although, you will not remember this story once you're born. This will be your journey through life..."

Then God shared the following story with the angel.

A young mother set her foot on the path of her life.

"Is this the long way?" she asked her guide.

"Yes, and the way is hard. You will be old before you reach the end of it. But the end will be better than the beginning," replied the guide.

The young mother was happy and she could not believe that anything could be better than these years. So, she followed the path and soon started playing with her children. She fed them and bathed them and taught them how to tie their shoes and ride a bicycle and reminded them to feed the dog and do their school homework and brush their teeth. The sun shone on them and the young mother cried with pride when she watched them grow.

"Nothing will ever be lovelier than this," she thought.

Then the nights came and the storms came and the path was sometimes dark, and the children shook with fear and the cold. The mother drew them close and covered them with her arms.

"Mother, we are not afraid. As long as you are near, no harm can come to us," said the children.

The morning came and there was still a hill ahead to climb. The children climbed the hill and grew weary. The mother was also weary. But, at all times, she said to her children:

"A little patience and we are there."

So, the children climbed and as they climbed, they learned to weather the storms. And with this, she gave them strength to face the world. Year after year she showed them compassion, understanding, hope, but most of all, unconditional love. When they reached the top, they said:

"Mother, we would not have done it without you!"

The days went on and the weeks turned into months and the months into years. The mother grew old and her hair began to turn silver; she became little and bent. But her children grew tall and strong and walked with courage and confidence. When the mother lay down at night she looked up at the stars.

"This is a better day than the last. My children have learned so much and are now passing these lessons onto their children."

When the way became rough for her, they lifted her, and gave her their strength just as she had given them hers. One day, they came to a hill and beyond the hill they could see a shining road and golden gates flung open wide.

"I have reached the end of my journey. I now know the end is better than the beginning. You, my children can walk with dignity and pride, with your heads held high, and so can your children after you," said the mother.

The children responded, "You will always walk with us, Mother, even when you have gone through the gates. We will never forget you and we will always love you. We know you will be waiting for us when our journey ends and we walk through those gates."

The children stood and watched her as she went on alone and the gates closed after her.

"We cannot see her, but she is with us still. A mother like ours is more than a memory. She is a living presence," said the children.

The angel's eyes brightened; her face expressed a wide smile. She laid her head on God's shoulder. He stroked her head.

"Now, go and find Gabriel and let him know that you are now ready to do your work."

The angel jumped up with a big grin and ran to find Gabriel. As she rushed off, she turned to God and asked, "How long will it be before I am sent to Earth, Father?"

"Nine months, my child."

Dear reader, your mother is always with you. She is the whisper of the leaves as you walk down the street. She is the smell of certain foods you remember that she cooked for you. She is the flowers you pick and the fragrance of the perfume she wore. She's the cool hand on your brow when you're not feeling well. She's your breath in the air on a cold winter's day. She is the sound of the rain that lulls you to sleep. She is the colors of the rainbow and she is Christmas morning.

Your mother lives inside your laughter, and she's crystallized in every teardrop you shed. A mother shows every emotion: happiness, sadness, fear, jealousy, love, hate, anger, helplessness, excitement, joy, sorrow---and all the while, she's hoping and praying that you will only know the good feelings in life. She's the place you came from; she's your first home and she's the map you follow with every step you take. She's your first love, your first friend, even your first enemy, but nothing on Earth can separate you from your mother's love; not time, not space, not even death!

Daniel's Mission

One day when I was having lunch at my favorite restaurant with two of my friends, we were making small talk and looking out the picture window. The quaint restaurant was located just off the corner of the town square. While looking out the window across the street from the restaurant, walking into town I saw a man who appeared to be carrying all his worldly goods on his back. He was carrying a well-worn sign that read, "I will work for food."

My heart sank when I saw the man. It was unusual to see what I considered a homeless man in that part of town. I brought him to the attention of my friends and I noticed that others in the restaurant had stopped eating to focus on the man. They shook their heads in a mixture of sadness and disbelief. My friends and I continued our meal but his image lingered in my mind. My friends and I finished our meal and went our separate ways. I had errands to do and quickly set out to accomplish them. I glanced toward the town square, looking somewhat halfheartedly for the strange visitor. I was fearful, knowing that seeing him again would trigger some response in me. I had spent some time working with an organization that provided food, clothes and shelter to homeless people, and it had always made me sad. Sometimes, I felt guilty that I had so much and they seemingly had so little.

I drove through town and saw nothing of him. I made some purchases at a store and got back in my car. Deep within me, the Spirit of God kept speaking to me:

"Don't go back to the office until you've at least driven once more around the square."

With some hesitancy, I headed back into town. As I turned the square's third corner, I saw him. He was standing on the steps of the store-front church, going through his backpack. I stopped and looked, feeling both compelled to speak to him, yet wanting to drive on. The empty parking space on the corner seemed to be a sign from God, an invitation for me to park my car.

I pulled into the parking space, got out of the car and approached the man.

"Are you looking for the pastor of this church?" I asked.

"No, not really," he replied. "I'm just resting."

"Have you eaten today?"

"Oh, I ate something early this morning."

"Would you like to have lunch with me?"

"Do you have some kind of work I could do for you?"

"No work," I replied. "But I would like to take you to lunch."

"Sure," he replied with a smile.

As he began to gather his things, I asked him some questions.

"Where are you headed?"

"St. Louis."

"Where are you from?"

"Oh, all over; mostly from Florida."

"How long have you been walking?"

"Fourteen years," came the reply.

By then, I was sure I had met someone unusual. I don't usually talk to strangers or seek them out and offer to take them to lunch as I had done with this stranger. But it was something spiritual about him that had drawn me to him the moment I first saw him through the restaurant's picture window.

We sat across from each other in the same restaurant I had left earlier when I first saw him. He told me his name was Daniel and that he was thirty-eight years old. His face was weathered slightly beyond his thirty-eight years. His eyes were dark, yet clear. He spoke with an eloquence and an articulation that were startling. He removed his jacket to reveal a bright red tee-shirt with the words "Jesus is The Never-Ending Story."

Then Daniel's story began to unfold. He had seen rough times early in life. He had made some wrong choices and reaped the consequences. Fourteen years earlier, while backpacking across the country, he had stopped on the beach in Daytona, Florida. He had tried to hire on with some men who were putting up a large tent and some microphones and recording equipment. He thought the tent was for a concert. He was hired by the organization setting up the tent but he soon realized that the tent would not house a concert, but would hold revival services and in those services, while working there, he saw life more clearly and he gave his life to God.

"Since then, nothing has been the same in my life," he said. "I felt the Lord telling me to keep walking, and so I did, some fourteen years now."

"Ever think of stopping?" I asked.

"Oh, once in a while, when traveling and walking seem to get the best of me. But God has given me this calling. I give out Bibles. That's what's in my sack. I work to buy food and Bibles and I give them out when and where His Spirit leads."

I sat amazed at this man called Daniel. My homeless friend was not homeless, after all. He was on a mission and lived this way by choice. A question burned inside of me for a moment, and then I asked:

"What is it like to walk into a town where you don't know anyone, you're carrying all your possessions on your back and you're carrying this sign indicating you're homeless? How do people respond to you?"

"It was humiliating at first. People would stare and make comments. Once, someone tossed me a piece of half-eaten bread and made a gesture that certainly didn't make me feel welcome. But then it became humbling to realize that God was using me to touch lives and change people's concepts of other folks like me."

My concept was changing too. We finished our dessert and gathered his things. Just outside the door he paused, turned to me and said:

"Come Ye blessed of my Father and inherit the Kingdom I've prepared for you. For when I was hungry you gave me food, when I was thirsty you gave me drink; I was a stranger and you took me in."

He then smiled, showing white even teeth. His face seemed to light up with his smile. I felt as if we were on holy ground.

"Could you use another Bible?" I asked.

He said he preferred a certain translation, which he named, the King James Version. He said it traveled well and was not too heavy to carry. It was also his personal favorite.

"I've read through it fourteen times," he said.

"I'm sure we've got one of those. Let's stop by our church and get one."

He got into my car and I drove to my church. I was able to find my new friend a KJV copy of the Bible and he seemed grateful.

"Where are you headed from here?" I asked.

"Well, I found a map on the back of an amusement park coupon. That's where I am going."

"Are you hoping to be hired there for a while?"

"No, I just figured I should go there. I thought maybe someone there might need a Bible."

He smiled, and the warmth of his spirit radiated the sincerity of his mission. I drove him back to the town square where we had met two hours earlier. As we drove, it started to rain. When we reached the town square I parked, and he got out, then started unloading his backpack and the handbag he carried that resembled an overnight bag. *How tiresome it must be to walk, carrying those bags!* I thought.

He pulled a notebook from one of his bags.

"Will you sign my autograph book?" he asked. "I like to keep messages from folks I meet during my journey."

I wrote in his little book that his commitment to his calling had touched my life. I encouraged him to stay strong. I left him with a verse of scripture from Jeremiah:

"I know the plans I have for you, declared the Lord; plans to prosper you and not to harm you; plans to give you a future and a hope."

"Thanks, friend," he said. "I know we just met and we're really only strangers, but I love you with the love of Jesus."

"I know," I said. "I love you too."

"The Lord is good!"

"Yes, He is! How long has it been since someone hugged you?" I asked.

"It's been a long time," he replied.

And so, on the busy street corner in the drizzling rain, my new friend and I embraced and I felt deep inside that I had been changed. He put his bags on his back, smiled his winning smile and said:

"See you in the New Jerusalem."

"I'll be there!" was my reply.

He continued on his journey. Heading away with his sign dangling from his backpack where he kept his Bibles, he stopped, turned and said:

"When you see something that makes you think of me, will you pray for me?"

"You bet!" I shouted back.

"God bless you!" he said, waved and continued on his journey.

And that was the last I saw of Daniel. Later that evening as I left my office, the wind blew strong. The cold front had settled hard upon the town. I bundled up and hurried to my car. As I sat back and reached for the emergency brake, I saw a pair of well-worn, brown work gloves neatly laid over the length of the handle. I picked them up and thought of my friend and wondered if his hands would stay warm that night without them. Then I remembered his words:

"If you see something that makes you think of me, will you pray for me?"

Today his gloves lay on my desk in my office. They help me to see the world and its people in a new way, and they help me remember those two hours I spent with my unique friend and to pray for his ministry.

"See you in the New Jerusalem," he had said.

"Yes, Daniel, I know I will." I repeat to myself every time I recall our last exchange.

The moral of this story is, never judge a person by how he or she looks. God's angels come in all forms. God made us all in His image. When you see a person who appears to be homeless, pray for them. You don't know their story.

Donavon's Letter

Nanette drove her son Donavon to the hospital for an operation on his brain. It was going to be just another of many he'd had since being born. Donavon had a rare cancer that caused him to require care twenty-four hours a day. He was ten years old and had endured pain beyond anything his parents thought possible for a young child to suffer. Yet, he never complained. Donavon was constantly asking his mother how she felt rather than focusing on his own declining health.

Nanette sat in the room designated for parents and waited for the doctor to come and, as he usually did, to advise her that the procedure was over and Donavon was resting in the recovery room before being taken back into his private room. Nanette jumped up from her seat as soon as she saw Dr. Layton, the surgeon who had cared for Donavon since birth, come out of the operating room. Donavon referred to Dr. Layton as his friend.

"How is my little boy? Is he going to be all right? When can I see him? Did everything go alright this time, Doctor?"

Nanette was nervous and fearful about the doctor's answers to her questions. Something in Dr. Layton's expression, the sad look in his eyes in particular, conveyed to Nanette that something was wrong this time.

"I'm sorry. We did all we could, but Donavon didn't make it this time."

Dr. Layton had practiced medicine for over twenty years, and he still couldn't get accustomed to children dying, children he sometimes felt powerless to save. He tried to steady his voice as he attempted to comfort Nanette.

She fell to her knees and cried uncontrollably. Doctor Layton felt helpless. He understood her pain. He had heard those cries from parents many times during his years of practicing medicine.

"Why do little children get cancer? Doesn't God care anymore? Where were you, God, when my son needed you?" Nanette lamented between sobs.

Would you like some time alone with your son? One of the nurses will be out in a few minutes to take you to him before he's transported to the university."

Nanette asked the nurse to stay with her while she said goodbye to her son. She ran her fingers lovingly through his thick red curly hair.

"Would you like a lock of his hair?" the nurse asked.

Nanette nodded her assent.

The nurse cut a lock of Donavon's hair, put it in a plastic bag and handed it to Nanette.

Nanette smiled bitterly and said, "It was Donavon's idea to donate his body to the university for study. He said it might help somebody else. At first, I said no, but Donavon said, 'Mom, I won't be using my body after I die. Maybe it will help some other little boy to spend one more day with his mom.'

"My Donavon had a heart of gold. He was always thinking of someone else, always wanting to help others if he could."

Shortly after, Nanette walked out of the Children's Mercy Hospital for the last time, after spending most of the last six months there. She put the bag with Donavon's belongings on the seat beside her in the car. The drive home was difficult. It was even harder for Nanette to enter the empty house. Not being able to handle Donavon's debilitating illness and the financial responsibility associated with the mounting medical bills, Donavon's father had left when Donavon was five years old. Nanette had tried to be both mother and father to her son whom she adored.

Nanette carried Donavon's belongings and the plastic bag with the lock of his hair to her son's room. She started placing his model cars and his other personal things exactly where he had always kept them. She lay on his bed, hugged his pillow and cried herself to sleep. It was midnight when

Nanette awoke. Lying beside her on the bed was a folded letter.

"Dear Mom, I know you're going to miss me, but don't think that I will ever forget you or stop loving you just because I'm not around to tell you that I love you. I will always love you, Mom, even more with each day. Someday, we will see each other again. Until then, if you want to adopt a little boy so you won't be so lonely, that's okay with me. He can have my room and my stuff to play with. But if you decide to get a girl instead, she probably wouldn't like the same things we boys do. You'll have to buy her some dolls and stuff that girls like.

"Grandma and Grandpa met me as soon as I got here and gave me a tour of Heaven, but it will still take a long time for me to see everything. The angels are so cool. I love to watch them fly. And you know what? Jesus doesn't look like any of His pictures. Yet as soon as I saw him, I knew who he was. Jesus himself took me to see God and guess what, Mom, I got to sit on God's knee and talk to Him like I was somebody important. That's when I told Him that I wanted to write you a letter to tell you goodbye. But I already knew that wasn't allowed.

"Well, you know what, Mom? God handed me some paper and His own personal pen to write you this letter. I think Gabriel is the name of the angel who is going to deliver this letter to you. God told me to give you the answer to one of the questions you asked Him at the hospital: 'Where was He when I needed Him?'

"God said He was in the same place with me as when His son Jesus was on the cross. He was right there, as He always is with all His children. Oh, by the way, Mom, no one else but you can see what I've written in this letter. To everyone else this is just a blank piece of paper. Isn't that cool? I have to give God His pen back now. He needs it to write some more names in the Book of Life.

"Tonight, I get to sit at the table with Jesus for supper. I'm sure the food will be great. Oh, I almost forgot to tell you, I

don't hurt anymore. The cancer is all gone. I'm glad because I couldn't stand that pain anymore and God couldn't stand to see me hurt so much either. That's when He sent the Angel of Marcy to the hospital to get me. The Angel said I was a special delivery! How about that? Signed with love from God, Jesus, and Me."

Nanette woke up and sat straight up in bed. She had fallen asleep on Donavon's bed. She looked around the room, feeling the presence of her son. Laying on the bed was a folded piece of paper. She opened it and it was blank but she knew what was written on the paper. She had read it in her dream. The paper hadn't been there when she first lay down. She smiled, hugged it to her chest and went back to sleep dreaming of the day when she would see her son again.

Lessons of Life

When things in your life seem almost too much to handle, when twenty-four hours in a day are not enough to complete all the things you need to accomplish, when you are overwhelmed with the complexities of life, remember the following little story about the mayonnaise jar and the two cups of coffee.

One day, a professor stood before his adult philosophy class and placed some items in front of him. When the class began, keeping silent, he picked up a large, empty mayonnaise jar and began to fill it with golf balls. He then asked the students if the jar was full.

They agreed it was.

The professor then picked up a box of small pebbles and poured them into the jar with the golf balls. He lightly shook the jar and the pebbles rolled into the open spaces between the golf balls. Again, he asked the students if the jar was full.

They agreed it was.

Next, the professor picked up a box of sand and poured the sand into the jar with the golf balls and pebbles. The sand filled up all the other open spaces in the jar.

Once again, the professor asked the students if the jar was full.

The students responded with a unanimous, "Yes!"

The professor then produced two cups of coffee from under the table and poured the entire contents into the jar, effectively filling the empty space between the sand.

The students laughed!

"Now," said the professor as the laughter subsided, "I want you to recognize that this jar represents your life. The golf balls are the important things in your life such as family, children, health, friends, and favorite passions. These are things that if everything else was lost and only they remained, your life would still be full.

"The pebbles are the things that matter, such as your job, your house, your car. You may not want to do without them, but, if necessary, you could.

"The sand represents everything else in your life; the small stuff. If you put the sand into the jar first, there will be no room for the pebbles or the golf balls. The same goes for life. If you spend all your time and energy on the small stuff, you will never have room for the things that are truly important to you."

The students applauded with understanding.

"So," continued the professor, "Pay attention to the things that are critical to your happiness. Play with your children. Take time to get medical checkups. Take your partner out to dinner. There will always be time to clean the house and fix the dripping faucet. Take care of the golf balls first––the things that really matter. Set your priorities; the rest is just sand."

One of the students raised her hand and inquired about what the coffee represented.

The professor smiled.

"I'm glad you asked! It just goes to show you that no matter how full your life may seem, there's always room for a cup of coffee with a friend."

Angel in the Rain

Every Sunday afternoon after the morning services at the Grace Memorial Baptist Church, the senior pastor, Pastor Anderson, and his eleven-year-old son, William, went throughout their town and handed out pamphlets with the word of God from scriptures of the Bible written on them.

This particular Sunday afternoon, as time came for Pastor Anderson and his son to go to the streets with their pamphlets, it was frigid cold outside with pouring rain. William bundled up in his warmest clothes, eager to get started.

"Okay, Dad, I'm ready." William said.

"Ready for what?" asked Pastor Anderson.

"Dad, it's time we gather our pamphlets and go out to meet the people. Somebody out there needs us. They may need a word from God."

His father thought that William was much wiser than his young years reflected but said, "Son, it's cold outside and it's pouring down with rain. You could catch pneumonia in this weather! No, today is a day to stay inside."

William gave his father a surprised look.

"But, Dad, can't people's souls still get lost while it's raining?"

"Son, I understand what you're saying and I agree, but I'm not going out in this weather. There's probably nobody out there anyway; it's raining too hard. The only people out on a day like this are people who are homeless."

"But don't homeless people need to know about God?" asked William.

Pastor Anderson insisted the weather was too cold for him to go outside.

Despondently, William persisted, "Dad, then can I go alone? Please?"

Pastor Anderson hesitated for a moment. He was reluctant to let his son go out in such bad weather. But William pleaded with his father to allow him to go.

"Alright, Son, you can go. Here are the pamphlets, but please be careful. You promise?"

"Thanks, Dad, I promise I'll be careful."

With that, William was off and out into the rain. He walked the streets of the town going door to door handing everybody he met in the streets a gospel pamphlet. After two hours of walking in the cold rain, he was soaking, bone-chilled wet and down to his very last pamphlet. He stopped on a corner and looked for someone to give the last pamphlet to. But the streets were deserted. Everyone was staying indoors because of the weather.

"Dad was right!" he muttered.

Then he turned toward the first home he saw and started up the sidewalk to the front door and rang the doorbell. Nobody answered. He rang the doorbell again and again. Still, no one answered. He waited but still no answer. Finally, the eleven-year-old trooper, cold from the rain, turned to leave and started down the steps, but as he began to walk down the steps, something inside of him stopped him. It was a compelling feeling that wouldn't let him leave the front porch of the house. A small voice inside of his head told him not to leave.

He turned around, went back to the door and rang the doorbell again. He couldn't understand this feeling of urgency. When he still didn't get an answer, he banged on the door with his fist. He waited; he didn't understand why, but a feeling inside was holding him there on the front porch! He rang the doorbell again and this time the door slowly opened. Standing in the doorway was a sad-looking elderly lady.

"What can I do for you, son?" she asked softly.

With radiant eyes and a smile that lit up her world, the little boy spoke:

"Ma'am, I'm sorry if I disturbed you, but I just wanted to tell you that Jesus really does love you, and I came to give you my last gospel pamphlet which will tell you all about Jesus and His great love."

William handed the woman his last pamphlet, smiled and turned to leave. She called to him as he walked down the steps.

"Thank you, son! And God bless you!"

"God bless you too!" replied William.

He waved goodbye and headed home.

The following Sunday morning in church, Pastor Anderson was in the pulpit. As the service began, he spoke to the congregation.

"Does anybody have a testimony they want to share?"

He waited for a response.

Slowly, in the back row of the church, an elderly lady stood to her feet. As she began to speak, a look of radiance came from her face.

"No one in this church knows me. I've never been here before. You see, before last Wednesday I was not a Christian. My husband died some time ago, leaving me alone in this world. I don't have any other family. Last Wednesday, being a particularly cold and rainy day, it was even more cold in my heart. At that time, I had come to the end of the line where I no longer had any desire or hope or will to live. So, I took a rope and a chair and went upstairs into my attic. I fastened the rope securely to a rafter in the roof, and then I stood on a chair and fastened the other end of the rope around my neck. Standing on that chair, I felt so lonely and brokenhearted. I was about to leap off the chair, when suddenly the loud ringing of my front door bell startled me. I thought, I'll wait a minute and whoever it is will go away.

"I waited and waited but the ringing of the doorbell seemed to get louder and more persistent. Then the person stopped ringing the doorbell and started banging loudly on the door. I thought to myself again, who on earth could that be? Nobody ever rings my bell or comes to visit me.

"I was annoyed at the interruption. I loosened the rope from my neck and started to the front door, and, all the while, the bell kept ringing louder and louder. When I opened the door and looked out, I could hardly believe my eyes. There on my front porch stood the most radiant, angelic little boy I had ever seen. His smile, oh, I could never describe it to you. The words that came from his mouth caused my heart that had long been dead, to leap into life.

"With a cherub-like voice, he said, 'Ma'am, I just came to tell you that Jesus really does love you.'

"He gave me this gospel pamphlet that I now hold in my hand. As the little angel disappeared back out into the cold rain, I closed my door and slowly read every word of this gospel pamphlet. Then I went up to my attic to get my rope and my chair. I wouldn't need them anymore. I knelt on my knees and prayed. When I stood up, I felt a peace I've never felt before. I felt loved. I am now a happy child of the King. Since the address of your church was on the back of this gospel pamphlet, I have come here to personally say thank you to God's little angel who came just in the nick of time and by so doing, spared my soul from an eternity in Hell."

The elderly lady began to cry. There was not a dry eye in the church. As shouts of praise and honor to the King resounded off the rafters of the building, Pastor Anderson came from the pulpit and went to the front pew where William, the little angel, was seated. He took his son in his arms and sobbed.

Probably no church has had a more glorious moment, and probably this universe has never seen a father that was more filled with love and pride for his son—except one.

Keep Your Fork

There was a young woman who had been diagnosed with a terminal illness and had been given three months to live. As she was getting her things in order, she contacted the pastor of her church and asked him to come to her home to discuss certain aspects of her final wishes. The young woman had been a faithful member of the pastor's growing congregation, and it was difficult for him to visit her knowing that in a few months her brief stay on Earth would end. However, it was his duty to bring comfort to a heart of sorrow; therefore, he put his personal feelings aside and visited the young woman at her home.

She told him which songs she wanted sung at her funeral, what scriptures she would like read, what she wanted said in her eulogy and what outfit she wanted to be buried in. Everything was in order according to her satisfaction, and the pastor was preparing to leave when the young woman suddenly remembered she had forgotten to mention to the pastor something very important to her.

"Pastor, there's one more thing," she said excitedly.

"What's that?" the pastor replied.

"This is very important to me," the young woman continued, "I want to be buried with a fork in my right hand."

The pastor stood looking at the young woman, not knowing quite what to say.

"That surprises you, doesn't it?" the young woman asked.

"Well, to be honest, I'm puzzled by your request," said the pastor.

The young woman began to explain her request.

"My grandmother once told me this story and from that time on I have always tried to pass along its message to those I love and those who are in need of encouragement. In all my years of attending social events and dinners, I always remember that when the dishes of the main course were being cleared, someone would inevitably lean over and say, 'Keep your fork.'

"It was my favorite part of the event because I knew that something better was coming, something wonderful for desert and with substance, something I would enjoy.

"So, I just want people to see me there in the casket with a fork in my hand and I want them to wonder, 'What's with the fork?' Then I want you to tell them: 'Keep your fork, the best is yet to come.'"

The pastor's eyes welled up with tears of joy as he hugged the young woman goodbye. He knew this would be one of the last times that he would be able to communicate with her in the manner in which they had done that day. She was getting progressively weak and her illness was rapidly taking control of her mind and body. But he also knew that the young woman had a better grasp of Heaven than he did. She had a better grasp of what Heaven would be like than many people twice her age, with twice as much experience and knowledge. She knew that something better was coming.

At her funeral, as people walked by the young woman's casket and saw the beautiful pink dress she was wearing and the fork in her right hand, they were puzzled. Over and over, the pastor heard the question, "What's with the fork?" and over and over he smiled as he answered them.

During his message, the pastor told the people of the conversation he'd had with the young woman shortly before she died. He told them about the fork and what it symbolized to her. He told them how he could not stop thinking about the fork and that they probably would not be able to stop thinking about it either.

He was right. So, the next time you reach for your fork, remember this wise young woman, and let her remind you that the best is yet to come...

The Smell of Rain

A cold March wind danced around the dead of night in Dallas, Texas as the doctor of the local hospital walked into the small hospital room of Diana Blessing. She was still groggy from the surgery. Her husband, David, held her hand as they braced themselves for the latest news. They had tried to be strong for each other, both feeling the ache in their hearts.

That afternoon of March 10, 1991, complications had forced Diana, only twenty-four weeks pregnant, to undergo an emergency cesarean to deliver their new daughter, Dana Lu Blessing. At twelve inches long and weighing only one pound and nine ounces, they already knew that she was perilously premature. Still, the doctor's soft words dropped like a bomb.

"I don't think she's going to make it," he said as kindly as he could, trying to inflict as little pain as possible to the already distressed couple.

"There's only a ten-percent chance that she will live through the night and even then, if by some slim chance she does make it, her future could be a very cruel one," continued the doctor.

Numb with disbelief, David and Diana listened as the doctor described the devastating problems Dana would likely face if she survived. She would never walk, she would never talk, she would probably be blind, and she would certainly be prone to other catastrophic conditions such as cerebral palsy or even complete mental retardation that would require complete support of her daily living functions.

"No! No!" was all Diana could say.

She buried her face in her husband's shoulder and they both cried. She and David, with their five-year-old son Dustin, had long dreamed of the day they would have a baby girl and become a family of four. Now, within a matter of hours, that dream was slipping away.

As those first days passed, a new agony set in for David and Diana. Because Dana's underdeveloped nervous system was essentially raw, the lightest kiss or caress only intensified her discomfort, so they couldn't even cradle their tiny baby girl against their chests to offer her the strength of their love. All they could do, as Dana struggled alone beneath the ultraviolet light in a tangle of tubes and wires, was to pray that God would stay close to their precious little girl.

There was never a moment when Dana suddenly grew stronger. David and Diana were thankful that at least she wasn't getting weaker. As long as she stayed the same, there was hope. But as the weeks went by, she did slowly gain an ounce of weight here and an ounce of strength there. At last, when Dana turned two months old, her parents were able to hold her in their arms for the very first time.

Two months later, although the doctors continued to gently but grimly warn David and Diana that Dana's chances of surviving, much less living any kind of normal life, were next to zero, Dana went home from the hospital, just as her mother had predicted.

Five years later, when Dana was a petite but feisty young girl with glittering gray eyes and an unquenchable zest for life, she showed no signs whatsoever of any mental or physical impairment. Simply, she was everything a little girl can be and more. But that happy ending is far from the end of her story.

One blistering afternoon in the summer of 1996 when Dana was seven-years-old, she was sitting in her mother's lap in the bleachers of a local ball park near her home, where her brother Dustin's baseball team was practicing. As always, Dana was chattering nonstop with her mother and several other adults sitting nearby when she suddenly fell silent.

Moments later, hugging her arms across her chest, little Dana asked, "Do you smell that?"

Smelling the air and detecting the approach of a thunderstorm, Diana replied, "Yes, it smells like rain."

Dana closed her eyes and again asked, "Do you smell that?"

Once again, her mother replied, "Yes, I think we're about to get wet. It smells like rain."

Still caught in the moment, Dana shook her head, patted her thin shoulders with her small hands and loudly announced, "No, it smells like Him! It smells like God when you lay your head on His chest."

Tears blurred Diana's eyes as Dana happily hopped down from her mother's lap to play with the other children.

Before the rains came, her daughter's words confirmed what Diana and all the members of the extended Blessing family had known, at least in their hearts, all along, during those long days and nights of her first two months of her life, when her nerves were too sensitive for them to touch her. God was holding Dana to His chest and it was His loving scent that she remembered so well.

Home for Christmas

Lucille, her older brother Paul and their mother and father, Leon and Ida Drake, lived on a one-acre farm in a two-room wooden cabin in a town in Alabama called Clarksville. Using logs from trees they had cut down on the property, Leon's brother, Melvin, had helped Leon build the cabin; however, there wasn't any indoor plumbing in the cabin for drinking, bathing, or washing dishes. They used fresh water brought from a local spring, and they built an outhouse in the back of the cottage.

Lucille and Paul often talked about how one day they would leave the farm when they became adults. When they were very young, the children slept in the same room on two cots. When they became teenagers, Paul slept in the kitchen by the stove on a small cot and Lucille still slept in the small bedroom they had shared. The two siblings were very close. Lucille's complexion was dark and she wore her natural curly hair short. Her father, whom she called "Papa," often teased her and called her, "Nappy-headed baby girl."

Lucille had always had a crush on George Russell, a little boy who lived on the next farm up the road from her family's farm. Lucille was a smart student in school while George, who also attended the same little two-room school house as Lucille, not only wasn't smart but he didn't take his education seriously either. He knew that Lucille liked him and he often used her affections for him to entice her to help him with his homework. George was light-complexioned and had green eyes. It was easy to discern that he was from a mixed family. His mother was black and his father was white. The rumor around town was that his mother had been raped by a white traveling salesman and, as a result, George was born. His mother washed and ironed white folks' clothes to support her and her son.

Lucille's brother's prize possession was an old pickup truck that was given to him when he was fifteen years old by an old man called Stoker, a white male who owned the land Paul and his family lived on. Paul and Lucille's mother, Ida, had worked for the Stoker family as a maid for years, and her husband, Leon, worked on the Stokers' farm as a farm-hand, then went home to work on his own small patch of land after work.

Although Paul wasn't a mechanic and knew nothing about fixing cars, he enjoyed tinkering with the truck every day after finishing his chores until he finally restored it to working condition. The little farm on which Paul and his family lived didn't yield much of an income for the Drake family; therefore, Paul had dropped out of school to work part-time in the local cotton mill. After work he would come home and help his father with the chores on their farm. After finishing his chores, he worked on his truck, which gave him much pleasure.

Lucille had shared with Paul her feelings for George Russell and she also confided in her best friend, Mandy. She told them of how she would sneak out of the house at night when her parents were asleep to meet George in the cornfield. She believed him when he said he loved her and promised that one day they would run away together. Paul warned Lucille to be careful about sneaking out to see George, because of how their father felt about "light-skin-colored folks." He thought they were arrogant and believed they thought they were better than colored people with darker skin. If Leon suspected that his daughter was having a romantic relationship with George, or even if he as much as heard her talking to her brother about George, he would fly into a rage.

Lucille learned that her father's mother had abandoned him when he was six years old and ran away from home with a "half-white city slickster," as his father said. Leon had been raised by his father and had spent his entire childhood listening to the anger his father spewed out about mixed-race colored people. Leon had brought that same wrath into his own marriage and projected it onto his children.

Then the circus came to town as it did every year and, as always, the first day was restricted to be attended by white folks only. The second day, colored people were allowed to attend the circus and so were white people. White folks could go to the circus on any day they wanted to go, but colored people could only go to the circus on designated days. The day before the circus arrived to town Lucille met George in the cornfield and told him that she thought she was pregnant. He was nervous and afraid of what her father would do when he learned of the pregnancy. Plus, he knew he couldn't afford to take care of Lucille and a baby. He couldn't even take care of himself. He promised Lucille that they would work it out. In the meantime, he was trying to figure a way out of the situation. He thought maybe he should deny the baby was his. After all, no one knew he had been secretly meeting Lucille.

When the circus left town, George went with it, having been hired to work with the animals. After George left, Lucille learned from her friend Mandy that she had heard rumors from other students at school; another young girl, who lived on a farm up the road from where Mandy lived, was also pregnant with George's baby and was due to give birth in the same month as Lucille. She also learned that George had always wanted to be an entertainer. He'd clearly figured that he would have a better chance of reaching his dream if he left Tennessee and went "up north."

When Lucille learned that she really was pregnant, she was afraid to tell her parents, especially her father. She knew he would beat her severely. He had warned Lucille that if she ever got "in the family way" and wasn't married, he would kick her out of the house. He would certainly put her out if he learned that not only was she pregnant, but the father of the baby was George Russell.

"You ain't got no business messin' wid no high-yeller niggas. Dey thinks dey is purty and dey don't want nothin' from no black-ass woman like you but what they can get. Ain't none of them no damn good," Lucille's father had said once. "You can tell that somebody in his family is white. Look at'em, ain't no nigga got no hair like dat. Now why do you think that some man dat looks white gonna pay attention to a nappy-headed nigga gal like you, if'en he ain't up to no good?"

Oftentimes, Leon would say to his wife, "That gal can get in the family way if she wants to, but ain't no bastard chile commin' in this heah house. Not whilst I'm head of dis house."

Lucille had heard that same speech many times during her young years. She never thought she would get pregnant out of marriage one day.

"We only had sex one time," Lucille said to her best friend, Mandy.

"But it only takes one time. What are you gonna do, Lucy? You're only sixteen. You ain't nothing but a baby yourself. How you gonna take care of a baby?" asked Mandy.

"I'm gonna run away and get me a job and take care of me and my baby. I'm gonna leave tonight when everybody is asleep, and I ain't never coming back. I love my mama but she depends on Papa for everything. She quit school in the ninth grade, and she don't know nothing except to clean house and wash and iron clothes for white folks. I ain't gonna raise my chile like that. My chile is gonna have a better life than I had on this run-down farm, working from sunup to sundown for a meager living," said Lucille.

Lucille had packed her clothes in a box earlier that day and hid them under her cot until everybody in the family was asleep. Later that night, when she heard her father snoring and she was sure he was sound asleep, she got up and prepared to leave. She pulled her box from under the cot that was her bed and headed for the front door. Just as she started out the door, she saw her mother standing by the door in the dark, waiting.

"You gonna leave widout tellin' yo mama goodbye?" Ida said softly, so she wouldn't wake her husband.

"Mama, you scared me. I thought you wuz sleep," said Lucille.

She was surprised to see her mother standing there in the dark.

"You think I would let my chile go away from home without hugging her mama? I know you got to go, 'cause I know you be wid chile in yo belly. But you need some money and a place to stay. I know you think I'm slow 'cause I dropped outta school and ain't never been nowhere ceptin' cross de creek. But I tried to be a good mama to you and your brother. I told my white lady, Mrs. Stoker, that you needed work and you need to move away from Clarksville. I been working for the Stoker family for many years. They been good to me. Mrs. Stoker saw me crying one day and asked me what was wrong. I told her about you being in the family way and that your papa wuz going to kick you outta the house when he finds out. I used to carry you to her house when you wuz just a wee baby. I had to clean and cook for her and I had to carry you wid me.

"She called her sister, Miss Cindy Braxton, in Durham, North Carolina. Miss Cindy says she needs a girl to help her with her children. Miss Cindy expects you to come to work for her. I met Miss Cindy and her husband Mr. Maurice when they visited the Stokers for Christmas one year. They're nice people. You'll like them. Miss Cindy said they got a maid's house in their backyard where you can stay until you find something else. Take this money I wuz saving for that new chair that I really don't need, and buy you a one-way bus ticket outta here."

"Mama, I can't take your money. You wuzn't saving for a new chair, you wuz saving for a new coat. I ain't gonna take your money."

"Mrs. Stoker gave me one of her coats. It ain't new, but it's betten' what I could afford. I'll be alright, Baby. Mama just needs to know that you'll be right. Please take the money. It will help me to sleep at night if I know that you at least have bus fare to get back home."

Lucille reluctantly took the money and hugged her mother. With the money, her mother had handed her a small note from Mrs. Stoker with the Braxtons' address.

"I'll be alright, Mama. Once I get to the Braxtons' house, I'll write to you. Don't let Papa know where I am. I don't want to fight with him no more," said Lucille.

Lucille hugged her mother again and walked out the door, down the steps that still needed painting, and down the pathway where vines hung over the fence. When she walked past her mother's flowerbed, she took one last look around her. She thought about the times she spent helping her mother pull weeds from among the flowers. She remembered watching her brother, Paul, who was three years older than Lucille, work on his old truck that was always breaking down. Paul always seemed to have time to answer Lucille's questions, and she always had a lot of questions to ask about boys. Lucille shook her head as if trying to erase the memories as she walked up the dirt road to the bus stop.

Back in the house, Ida had a strange feeling that she would never see her daughter again. She shook off the feeling, deciding it was just her mother's instinct not wanting to let go of her lastborn, her only daughter. Lucille had just turned sixteen, a week earlier.

Lucille went to Durham, North Carolina, arriving there just as the sun was coming up. She thought it was too early to go to the house where the Braxton family lived, so she sat inside the colored section of the bus station until the sun came up. When the sun was bright, Lucille asked the attendant in the bus station the directions to the address on Mrs. Stoker's note. Lucille was grateful that the Braxtons' house wasn't a long distance away from the bus depot. She couldn't afford a taxi so she walked along the long dusty road, carrying her suitcase.

Lucille was tired and her clothes were dusty when she reached the Braxtons' house. It was a large white house that sat on a hill. It reminded her of the houses on slave plantations she often read about. She felt apprehensive about entering the house through the front door, but because the house was so massive, she didn't know her way to the back door of the house where servants entered. She climbed the marble steps leading to the front door and knocked. A maid answered the door and looked quizzically at Lucille.

"Yes, what can I do for you?" she asked.

"My name is Lucille Drake. Mrs. Braxton's sister, Mrs. Stoker, told me to come here."

"Oh, you're that little girl who went and got herself in trouble. The missus told me to expect you. Come on in, she'll see you now."

Lucille walked into the beautiful house and was in awe of the decorations and furniture. Mrs. Braxton came into the room. She was a short, pleasant-looking woman with mixed gray hair cut short. She instructed the maid to explain to Lucille what her duties would be and where she would be staying. During their exchange, Lucille learned the maid's name was Dora.

Lucille followed Dora into the servant's quarters to put away her dust-covered luggage, change into clean clothes and begin her assigned duties. As it turned out, the job was easy to do. Her duties mainly involved caring for the children, and helping Dora to clean the house and wash and iron the family's clothes. At the end of the day, she would go to her little place in the backyard maid's quarters. By the light of the kerosene lamp, she'd often write to her mother so that she wouldn't worry.

Ida hid the letters from Lucille's father. He was still furious that she had left home. He thought that she had disgraced the family by getting pregnant and leaving home in the middle of the night. He had disowned her and forbidden Lucille's mother and brother to mention her name in his presence.

Lucille wanted to go home to visit her family, but Ida said it wasn't time yet. She told Lucille to wait and give her papa time to get over his anger.

Six months into her pregnancy, while working for the Braxton family, Lucille started having pains in her stomach. She had felt her baby stirring inside her stomach early into her pregnancy but hadn't felt any movement within the past few weeks. She didn't know anything about being pregnant and couldn't talk to her mother to ask questions. She was confused.

One day, Lucille was in the laundry room taking clothes from the washer when she doubled over with pain and collapsed to the floor moaning. As she fell, she reached for something to hold on to. A basin was sitting on the dryer. She reached for it and it fell to the floor making a loud crashing sound. Dora heard the noise and called to Lucille.

"Lucille, is everything alright? What's that noise? Did I hear something fall? You're not breaking anything, are you?" Dora shouted from another room.

Lucille didn't answer.

Dora called to Lucille again. "Lucille, did you hear me? Answer me, girl."

Still Lucille didn't answer. She was in too much pain.

Dora went into the laundry room and saw Lucille on the floor doubled up in pain and moaning. She rushed to her.

"Lucille, what's wrong?" she asked, then she saw the blood and the clear liquid flowing from under Lucille's body.

"Oh, my God!" shouted Dora.

"Miss Cindy! Miss Cindy! Come quick, something is wrong with Lucille," shouted Dora.

Cindy Braxton ran into the laundry room to find Lucille lying on the floor in a pool of blood. She rushed for the telephone and called Dr. Pinkton, who had been the Braxtons' family doctor for several years. Doctor Pinkton told Cindy to call an ambulance. He would meet them at the hospital.

Cindy called an ambulance and it took Lucille to the hospital. The baby had turned around in Lucille's womb. They got her to the hospital just in time to save Lucille's life, but she lost her baby.

Cindy contacted Ida and told her about Lucille's near-death experience while giving birth. Ida and Paul took the bus to Durham to visit Lucille while she was still in the hospital. Ida was shocked at how pale her daughter was. The doctor said it was because Lucille was small in stature and because she had lost a lot of blood. Mrs. Braxton told Ida that she could stay in Durham a few days while Lucille was in the hospital. While in Durham, Cindy allowed Ida to stay in the maid's quarters where Lucille had stayed while she worked for them.

Ida spent several days with her daughter, and, by then, Leon was furious that she'd been away from home for so long. Knowing her husband's temper, Ida thought that he would be angry if she stayed in Durham; however, she made up her mind that regardless of his feelings, she would not give in to his protestations. This time she felt that her daughter needed her more than Leon did.

Paul had stayed for two days and then returned to Clarksville to resume work at the local mill. When he returned home, Paul tried to talk to his father about Lucille.

"Pop! You should have seen Lucy. She looked so pale. Why is it that you are so stubborn and won't let her come home? She needs to be with her family. She's your only daughter and you're too self-centered to give in. She's in the hospital in the colored section and she needs her family," Paul said.

"Young man, don't you sass me. I'm the head of this family. I tell you what to do," said an angry, hostile Leon. He was furious that his son had sided with Lucille and he raised his hand as if he was going to strike his son.

"What, Pop! What're you going to do? You're going to ban me from the house too? You're going to kick me out of the family too?" said Paul.

Leon lunged at Paul.

"Pop, don't try it. I respect you but I won't allow you to hit me. I'm almost twenty years old! Do you really expect me to take a beating from you?" Paul asked.

Leon knew his son was right. He just waved his hands as if telling Paul to go away. Paul packed his bags and moved out of his parents' house that night.

Ida returned to Clarksville. She had to return to work. Cindy Braxton promised Ida that when Lucille was released from the hospital she was going to rest in the maid's quarters until she was well enough to return to her duties. Ida was grateful that Lucille was employed by such a caring family.

After three weeks, Lucille was released from the hospital and returned to the Braxtons' house. However, her health didn't improve. A few days later, she caught pneumonia and had to be readmitted to the hospital. Ida prepared to return to Durham to see her daughter.

By then, Leon had realized how sick his daughter really was. He thought about what Paul had said and finally understood that he had pushed both of his children away.

"Ida, go and get our daughter and bring her home. Tell my little girl I'm sorry and that her papa loves her. Tell her I want her to come home, and we'll take care of her like a family is supposed to do. You go now, Ida, and stay in Durham with our daughter for as long as it's necessary until she is strong enough to travel."

Ida went back to Durham to the hospital to see her daughter. Lucille was on oxygen and other tubes were in her arms. She could barely lift her head. When she heard her mother's voice, she opened her eyes and managed a weak smile.

"Hello, sweetheart. Your papa sends his love and begs you to forgive him. He says he wants his little girl to come home. He told me as soon as you are strong enough that I'm to bring you home," said Ida.

Lucille was glad to hear that her papa had forgiven her, but she was so weak she could hardly speak.

"I'm going to hurry and get well so I can come home," Lucille whispered feebly.

The doctor told Ida that because of Lucille's size and her declining health, she would have to stay in the hospital for a few weeks. Ida decided to return back home and prepare for her daughter's return. She would then return to Durham to get her daughter and bring her home. But Lucille didn't get better. She died a week later. Her parents couldn't afford to have her body shipped back to Clarksville. Ida, Leon, Paul, and Mrs. Stoker drove to Durham to attend Lucille's funeral that was held in the church where the Braxton family attended. It was a beautiful church.

"God doesn't discriminate," said the pastor at Lucille's funeral. "God made us all and little Lucille is at home with her baby son, who never got to see his mama here on Earth."

Although the Braxton family could convince the pastor of their church to hold Lucille's funeral there, the church's board of directors would not permit her body to be buried in their all-white cemetery. Up the street from the church that the Braxton family attended was Bethel Baptist, a church that was attended by a colored congregation. They allowed Lucille to be buried in their cemetery.

Ida, Leon, Paul, and Mrs. Stoker drove beck to Clarksville in silence. Neither knew what to say. Ida felt as if she was leaving her daughter in a lonely place where she would be all alone in death. Months passed, and, at some point, Paul moved back home to help his father on the farm.

It had now been many months since Lucille's death. One day, Arthur, a truck driver who had been driving a tractor trailer truck for more than ten years, was on the highway one cold, wintry, December night. Over the years, he had made many trips from Tennessee and North Carolina to California delivering farm products. This night he had been driving for several hours making stops along the way and he had gotten hungry. He planned to stop at the diner at the truck stop where the majority of the truckers ate because the diner served home-cooked food and wasn't stingy with the portions.

After Arthur finished eating, he sat in the diner talking to some of the other truckers. He then walked outside in the cold December weather, got into his truck and pulled out of the parking lot of the diner. It was just starting to snow. He didn't realize that he had stayed and talked for so long, and he wanted to make time on the highway. It was three days before Christmas and he had promised his seventeen-year-old daughter that he would be home before Christmas. He planned to drive for another three hours, then pull over, catch a few hours sleep in the cab of the truck, then continue on.

As he drove up the highway, he hadn't gotten more than two miles from his last stop when he saw a frail young woman standing on the side of the road waving for him to stop. The young woman didn't have a suitcase, and she was dressed only in a thin jacket, even though the snowy, December night air had turned cold. Arthur didn't usually stop for hitchhikers, but there was something different about this young woman. She didn't look like she should be out on the highway alone at night. Arthur thought that maybe the woman had been riding with someone and something happened to make her get out of the car. He pulled up beside her.

"Hello, young lady. What are you doing alone on a highway like this? You could be in danger standing all alone here. Can I give you a lift?"

The young woman smiled, and then he realized she was actually a teenager, about seventeen years old. She reminded him of his own daughter. He wasn't about to leave her stranded alone on a dark lonely highway in the middle of the night. Especially with the weather taking a turn for the worse, plus she wasn't dressed to be out in such weather.

"Yes, please. I'm on my way home for Christmas," the young woman said.

"Get in. I'll take you as far as I'm going," said Arthur.

Clutching her thin coat to shield herself from the cold December air and pulling the red scarf she was wearing closer around her neck, the young woman climbed into the truck.

"Thank you for being so kind," said the young woman.

As they drove, Arthur asked her why she was out on the highway alone at night. She told him that she was on her way home to spend Christmas with her family.

"I can't wait to get home, smell Mama's cooking, sit at the table with my family and put my arms around my papa's neck and tell him I love him. I wanted to go home for a long time but Mama said it wasn't time. But Papa said now it's time."

She told Arthur where she lived, in a little cabin on a farm, not far off the highway. Arthur had made up his mind that he was going to take her all the way to her house. It wasn't much out of his route, and he figured that he could still be home by Christmas. He hoped that if someone ever saw his daughter in such a predicament, they would help her in the same way. He continued to ask her questions about her family, and how she came to be stranded on the highway, but she didn't appear to want to answer his questions. She had only told him where she lived and nothing more. He decided not to insist that she talk.

When Arthur arrived at the next truck stop, he pulled into the parking lot. Parking the truck, he turned to the young woman who was still sitting silently and said, "I'm going in to get a cup of hot coffee. I'll be right back. At least, let me buy you some hot coffee."

She just smiled and shook her head to decline.

He went into the diner and purchased two cups of coffee. He thought if the young woman smelled the aroma of the steaming coffee, she would change her mind about not wanting any. However, when he returned to his truck, the young woman was gone. Only her red scarf was left on the seat of the truck. Arthur was puzzled. Where would a frail young girl go in the middle of the highway on a cold December night? He was concerned about her safety. He was afraid that something had happened to her. He was familiar with the way some truckers can entice young girls to get into their trucks so they could take advantage of them. The young woman appeared to be so frail and pale that she would not physically be able to defend herself. He got back into his truck and began to drive. He didn't stop until he reached the address where his young passenger had said she lived. He wanted to tell her family about her and to return her scarf.

He reached the girl's farm and knocked on the door of the cabin. It was the home of Leon and Ida Drake. They invited him inside.

"Hello, my name is Arthur Foster. I drive trucks for a living. While on the highway, I saw a young girl, about sixteen or seventeen years old, and she said she lives here and was on her way home for Christmas. We stopped up the road about fifteen or twenty miles from here. I went in a diner to get some coffee and left her sitting in my truck. When I returned with the coffee, she was gone. I stopped by to tell you because she was so young and frail, and she might be in danger. Plus, she only had on a thin coat. Perhaps you might want to call the police for help."

Leon and Ida just sat and listened to Arthur. He couldn't understand why they were smiling and didn't seem to be upset with what he was saying.

"Don't you understand? A young girl may be out there in trouble. Do you know her?"

Ida stood up and took a picture from the mantle and showed it to Arthur.

"Is this the young girl who was your passenger?" she asked.

"Yes! That's her. Is she your daughter? She may be in real trouble."

Ida pressed the picture close to her chest, tears rolling down her cheeks.

"This was our daughter, Lucille," said Leon, his voice trembling with emotional pain and grief. She died a year ago. You are the third person who comes to our home and tells us that they picked her up to bring her home. This time she was seen closer to home than the other two times. At least she's getting closer. Maybe next time she'll make it... then maybe she'll forgive this old fool for sending her away in the first place."

Arthur handed him her red scarf. With tears in his eyes, he hugged both Ida and Leon and left to get home to spend Christmas with his own family.

The following day was Christmas; Ida awakened and discovered that Leon was not in bed with her. She put on her robe and slippers and went to see where he was. As she passed the room that had been Lucille's bedroom, she saw Leon lying on the little cot where Lucille used to sleep, his eyes closed. Lucille's picture and the red scarf that she had left in Arthur's truck were laying on his chest embraced in his arms. Ida stood in the doorway looking at her husband. She walked into the room with tears in her eyes, bent down, kissed her husband and realized that he was dead. A smile was on his face.

"I guess our daughter made it home for Christmas, after all, and from the smile on your face, my husband, I guess she has forgiven you. Rest, my love, and save a place for me," whispered Ida and she kissed her husband on his forehead. Feeling the presence of their daughter in the room growing palpable, she blew a kiss in the air and whispered, "Mama loves you my baby girl... Merry Christmas to you and your papa."

The Feeling of Disrespect

Patricia Baldwin was the guest speaker at a conference of business women. Her topic was, "The Feeling of Disrespect." She shared with them her experiences of what she described as being disrespected.

"I often wonder why is it that people you don't know, such as nurses, clerks in some doctors' offices, and sometimes sales people whom you have never met, call you on the telephone and think it's permissible to refer to you by your first name. Sometimes it's obvious that I am old enough to be their mother, yet that fact doesn't deter them from addressing me by my first name. They obviously feel that it's permissible. Some of the white salesmen have even referred to me as Pat instead of Patricia.

"It infuriates me to be subjected to what I call disrespect. Some organizations where people execute this type of behavior have a way of making you feel not worthwhile. I understand, for example, how individuals who receive welfare benefits feel when spoken to in a patronizing manner. I was once one of those people.

"When you're in need and someone looks down their nose at you, or talk to you with disrespect—as if you are in that circumstance because you want to be, rather than because of unfortunate situations—you can't feel good about yourself.

"Some government agencies are considering putting into place programs that focus on building the self-esteem and self-confidence of their workforce. I contend that such programs should be provided for those individuals who are responsible for providing services to the workforce.

"When I was on welfare, I felt that people looked at me with ridicule when I went to the Welfare Department to get assistance and when I used food stamps to pay for food at the grocery store. The case workers at the Department of

Social Services were some of the people who made me feel subservient to them. The cashiers in the supermarkets and people in line who were paying for their food with cash or checks rolled their eyes at me when I paid for my groceries with food stamps. I felt that the opinion of people on welfare was that they were all black women who were lazy and without ambition.

"I am sometimes treated with disrespect today in 2021, just because I am a black woman, and I'm not even on welfare. I have waited in the doctor's office when the nurse or clerk referred to me by my first name; yet, when a white woman, who was obviously younger than me, walked into the office, that same nurse addressed the young white woman as 'Mrs.,' 'Miss.,' or 'Ms.' Whenever that happens, I am reminded of growing up in the South where it doesn't matter how old you are; if you are a member of the black race, you are called 'boy' or 'girl.' I always ask myself the question, 'How old does one have to be before they become a man or woman and no longer a boy or a girl if they are black?' The following story drives home the point I am trying to make concerning 'disrespect.'

"One of my colleagues, Constance, was in her seventies when one day she and her best friend Rhonda, and Rhonda's daughter, Sherrie, went into a department store to buy a pair of shoes. They looked at all the shoes on display and Constance selected two styles of shoes that she wanted to try on. The shoe clerk, who was a white man and appeared to be in his late twenties or early thirties, came to assist them. Constance pointed to the shoes she wanted and gave him her size. When he returned with the shoes, he handed them to her to try on. While standing watching Constance try on the shoes he heard Rhonda call her by her first name.

"'Constance, I like the way those look on your feet. How do they feel with those pointed toes?' Rhonda asked.

"'Yeah, how do those feel on your feet, Constance?' the salesman asked.

"Constance looked at him, a little annoyed that he had addressed her by her first name. It was obvious that he was much younger than she was, but that apparently didn't matter to him.

"'They feel a little tight, and my name is Mrs. Jackson,' she said.

"He ignored her comments and continued to address her by her first name. He apparently was trying to make a point that he was not going to address her as 'Mrs.'

"'I have another pair I think you might like, Constance. I'll be right back,' he said.

"He went into the back of the store and brought out another pair of shoes. Just for smartness he refused to refer to her by her last name.

"'Well, Connie, would you like to see something else?' he asked.

"'Only my friends and acquaintances refer to me by my first name and you are neither. Please call me Mrs. Jackson,' she said to him.

"Again, he ignored what she said.

"'Whata ya say, Connie? You want to see another pair?' he said.

"My friend was furious and insulted, but she tried to contain her anger.

"'Yes, I would like to see something else, but what is your name?' she asked.

"'My name is Mister Wall, just like that wall right here,' he responded.

"He had a smug look on his face and touched the wall with his opened hand to indicate to what he was referring to.

"'What is your first name?' Constance asked.

"'You don't need to know my first name. You may call me Mister Wall. I'll be back in a few minutes with another pair of shoes, Connie,' he said.

"He practically skipped into the stockroom to get more shoes. He appeared to be gloating as he rushed away. Constance was furious.

"Rhonda's daughter, Sherrie, who was approximately sixteen years old, said, 'He's only trying to be smart. He heard you tell him your name is Mrs. Jackson. That's why I hate white folks. They're always trying to put us down.'

"'All white folks aren't like that jack-ass,' Constance said.

"Constance said that she nodded her head in the direction the salesman had gone. He returned from the stockroom with boxes of shoes and proceeded to wait on another customer—a white woman—and he put the shoes on her feet instead of handing them to her as he had done Constance. He also referred to the white woman as 'Ma'am.' Constance thought about what Sherrie had said.

"'You're right! He is just trying to be smart, but I've got something for him,' she said to Sherrie.

"Then another salesman—a black man—came from the back of the store, holding boxes of shoes in each hand. Constance walked over to him.

"'Excuse me please,' she said.

"He stopped and peered at her over the boxes.

"'What's the name of that man over there waiting on the lady in the blue dress?' she asked.

"She pointed to the salesman who had said his name was Mister Wall.

"'Oh, you must mean Mister Wall,' the black man responded.

"'But what is his first name?' she asked.

"'You can call him Mister Wall. We all call him that,' said the black salesman.

"'Yeah, and he probably calls everybody else by their first names too,' she replied.

"The salesman looked at her as if she had two heads, and walked away. A saleswoman—a black woman—who was waiting on another person, looked at Constance, smiled, then rolled her eyes at the black salesman. Constance hadn't seen the saleswoman when they first entered the shoe department. The saleswoman was just returning to the area as if she was just coming on duty. She had heard Constance's conversation with the black salesman.

"'You must be talking about Mister Wall. Honey, he treats all black customers—especially black women—like he's doing them a favor by waiting on them. I wish one of them would complain to the manager. I complained once and he made it look like I was jealous of his sales. And that *Uncle Tom* over there is too scared of losing his job to say anything,' she said and nodded her head in the direction of the black salesman, who was now assisting another customer.

"Constance smiled at the saleswoman and said, 'Well, I'm not going to let him get away with his smartness. This time, he picked on the wrong woman.'

"Mister Wall then returned to inquire as to whether or not she was going to purchase the shoes.

"'Well, Connie, do you like'em? They're just what you asked for. Are you going to buy'em?' he said.

"'Yes, I am, but I'm not going to buy them if you'll get a commission from my purchase, Dog-Breath. You have insulted me and disrespected me from the moment I entered the shoe department. And you know what, Stuck-on-Stupid, why don't you skip your little bony self over there and help someone else. I no longer need or want your assistance,' she said.

"Constance then smiled, picked up her pocketbook and started to walk away.

"He didn't know what to say. He just stood there, looking at her with an expression of disbelief on his face.

"'I showed you these shoes. If you pay for them, I'm entitled to the commission,' he said.

"Then in a voice loud enough so other shoppers and sales people in that area could hear her, Constance said, 'What's the matter Garlic-Mouth? Don't you like being addressed with disrespect? I told you several times not to address me by my first name, and you're not even sure that the name you have been calling me really is my first name. You apparently insist on calling me whatever you want to call me. In that case, I have that same privilege. If you can call me what you want to call me, then I will call you what I want to call you. If you continue to address me as you so choose, I got some real doosies that I can call you. Now the next move is yours, Mr. Moose Mouth. By the way, I want to speak to the manager.'

"The black saleswoman went to get the store manager. The manager—a white man—came out of the back office. The manager apologized for Mister Wall. Then the manager took him into the back of the store and they didn't see Mister Wall anymore the entire time they were in the store. The saleswoman came over and gave Constance a high-five.

"'Honey, I sure do want to thank you. You just made my day. That man is the biggest racist here. But this time Mr. Wall met his match. I love it!' she said.

"Rhonda and Sherrie laughed so hard tears rolled down their cheeks. They left the store after she purchased the shoes from the woman sales clerk. She assured Constance that she would get the commission and not Mister Wall."

The White Shaggy Dog

Once, there was a man named Jasper, who had a white shaggy dog named Rover. No one knew what type of dog Rover was. He was a mixed breed—a mutt. Even the hair on Rover was shaggy. Everyone thought that Jasper was mean to Rover because late at night they could hear Rover barking and then hear him hollering. The neighbors thought that Jasper beat Rover because of Rover's incessant barking, which, presumably, annoyed Jasper. But every time someone saw Jasper, Rover was always with him, trotting at his heels. Sometimes, Jasper kept Rover tied up outside by the coal shed.

One night, Rover was tied outside and he kept barking and howling. The woman who lived next door, Mamie, was an alcoholic. Rover's barking was annoying her that night, so she decided to sneak over into Jasper's yard and cut the rope that was holding Rover so that he could hopefully go away and leave her in peace. Mamie crept out of her back door, and into Jasper's yard. She used her kitchen knife and cut the rope that was used to tie Rover to the coal shed. When Rover realized that he was free, he moved away from the spot for a bit, then went back to the same place where he was tied and laid down on the ground.

Mamie tried to make Rover run away, but he wouldn't go. He wouldn't leave his master. It appeared that he just didn't want to be restricted to where he could go. Mamie realized that Rover wasn't going to leave, and she thought he was just a dumb dog. He didn't have enough sense to run away when he had the chance, even though he was being abused and mistreated.

A week later, Jasper died. He lived alone and he didn't have any family. Therefore, not many people attended his funeral. The only people who were there were his neighbors and, of course, Rover.

When the funeral was over, Jasper's body was laid to rest in the cemetery not far from the mortuary. After everyone had left the cemetery, Rover remained laying on Jasper's grave. The neighbors tossed a coin to see who would get to keep Rover. The kids in the neighborhood had become attached to Rover. He was a friendly dog.

One cool Autumn night with a full moon, Mamie and her next-door neighbor, Walter, were walking home from the local café, and they spotted Rover walking on the other side of the street. He seemed to be headed toward the house where he once lived when Jasper was alive.

"That looks like Rover," said Mamie. "I wonder what he's doing loose this time of night. He could be hit by a car out here in the streets alone. I heard that the Boleware family took him after Jasper died. They've got five children. I know they don't know that Rover is out here wondering around in the streets alone. Come to think of it, Jasper's been dead for almost a month, and not once have I heard Rover bark and howl at night the way he used to do when Jasper was alive. I bet he misses him. Jasper found Rover when he was a tiny puppy – just days old. They've been together for a long time."

"Yeah! I kind of feel sorry for Rover," said Walter. "Every time I see him, he looks like he's waiting for Jasper to come and get him. I wish I could make him understand that Jasper won't be coming home no more. Tony Boleware said every time they can't find Rover they go over to his old house and find him out by the coal shed, seemingly waiting for Jasper to come home. Maybe we better get him and take him home before he gets hurt out here this late at night."

"I think you're right. Here, Rover! Come here, boy!" Mamie called.

"Here, boy. Come on, Rover!" shouted Walter.

Rover didn't pay any attention to Walter or Mamie and kept trotting as if he were going home.

Mamie called to him again, "Rover, Rover, come here, boy!"

Again, he didn't respond and kept walking toward his old house.

"Let's go and get him. We can take him back to the Bolewares' house. I bet they don't know he broke loose," said Mamie.

"Good idea! If they find him missing, they'll probably be worried about where he is. He's not a bad dog," said Walter.

Mamie and Walter ran across the street to get Rover.

"Good dog, good dog!" Walter said, trying not to panic Rover.

Mamie and Walter began to walk up to Rover talking to him in a soothing voice. Rover kept trotting as if he couldn't hear Mamie and Walter calling him. Just as they got to Rover and Walter reached for him, Rover turned to look at Mamie and Walter and, now, impossibly, it was Jasper's face that looked at them and Jasper's voice coming from Rover.

"Hello, Walter and Mamie, I'm on my way home," Rover said.

Mamie and Walter both screamed and ran, bumping into each other as they did so. No one believed their story, and after that night, no one saw Rover again. Mamie and Walter never took another drink of alcohol again and never forgot that Rover's face had changed into Jasper's face when he turned to look at them.

The Leaf

One night after working late, Garfield was walking home, whistling a tune that he had just heard on the radio from one of the houses he had passed. It was an autumn night; the wind was blowing and leaves were circling around and around as if they were playing the game that children often played called "Sally Go Round the Mulberry Bush."

I love the Fall; best of all seasons. It's the time of the year when Mother Nature is at her best, wearing all different colors and getting ready for Old Man Winter... thought Garfield.

As Garfield walked up the street, he noticed the leaves blowing all around him, circling him. He laughed and thought that Mother Nature was playing a game with him. Somewhere in the distance, he heard a clock strike twelve midnight.

Twelve o'clock midnight in October. That's when the witches and goblins are out. And there's a full moon out tonight. They say that ghosts walk the streets when there's a full moon... he mused with a chuckle.

As he continued walking, he noticed that a small pile of leaves seemed to be following him. Garfield kept whistling. He was trying not to notice the leaves and trying not to think of anything as foolish as ghosts.

"I'm a grown man. There's no such thing as ghosts. Come on, Garfield, don't be stupid. If the boys thought you were afraid of ghosts, they'd laugh at you right out of the plant. You've been working the midnight shift for five years. Don't start believing in ghosts now," he whispered to himself.

He began to laugh and talk out loud to himself, trying to pretend that he wasn't starting to feel uncomfortable.

Still, he couldn't shake the feeling that he was being followed. He kept looking back behind him, but there was no one in the street except him. As he walked, he looked over his shoulder, but no one was there. He was wearing a hat and a coat, and his hat felt as if it were being pulled off his head. He reached up and adjusted his hat and kept walking.

Garfield noticed that the same swirling cluster of leaves that had been following him almost a block away was still following. As he looked at the leaves, they parted and blew away except for one leaf that remained blowing in the wind just in front of him—except there was no wind. It had stopped blowing. The air was calm—too calm. It was an eerie calmness. Garfield reached for the leaf and tried to grab it, but it kept blowing out of his reach. His hat still felt as if it were being pulled off of his head, and he kept tugging at it to keep it on. Garfield began to sweat and quickened his pace. The leaf also began to float a little faster in front of him.

"This is no ordinary leaf. The wind has stopped blowing but that leaf still remains in the air in front of me. What the heck is happening?" Garfield whispered.

Garfield noticed that the night air had gotten very still and calm; not a leaf on the trees was stirring. His hat felt as if a giant wind was trying to blow it off of his head. He kept pulling on his hat to keep it on his head and now had to use both hands to hold it in place. All the while, the leaf kept floating in front of him. When Garfield finally reached his house, the leaf disappeared.

He ran onto his porch and couldn't get his key in the door; he was trembling too much with fear. He finally steadied his trembling hand enough to put the key in the lock and unlocked the door. He pushed the door open and rushed inside the house. When he finally got inside, he couldn't get his hat off his head. It wouldn't come off. He had to cut it off.

When his hat was finally off, he noticed that the band of the hat had left a mark like a ring around his head. For weeks he could not get rid of the indentation on his forehead that was made by the hat. No matter what he did he couldn't remove it. Finally, after three weeks had passed and the indentation wouldn't fade away, he went to visit his mother's grave and knelt down beside her tombstone.

"Mother, I love you. Please forgive me for not coming to your funeral. I just couldn't bear to say goodbye. I wanted to remember you as you were the last time I saw you. You were standing in the doorway, wearing a white apron, waving to me. Forgive me, Mama," he cried.

As he rose from his knees, the indentation on his forehead from the hat disappeared.

The Son

A wealthy man and his son loved to collect rare works of art. They had many expensive paintings in their collection. Their collection of paintings hung in various rooms throughout their home where the two of them often admired their collection of beautiful rare works of art. They lived in a part of the world that was ravaged by war. One year during the war, the rich man's son wanted to serve his country so he enlisted in the army and his platoon was sent to a foreign land to fight. The son was very courageous and was killed in battle while trying to rescue a fellow soldier. The father was notified of his son's death and grieved deeply. He was his only son.

A month after his son's death, just before Christmas, there was a knock on the door of the wealthy man's mansion. When he opened the door, there stood a young man with sad eyes, in a soldier's uniform, holding a large package in his hands.

"Hello, sir, you don't know me, but I'm the soldier whom your son tried to save, losing his own life. Your son not only saved my life, but the lives of many others that day. He was carrying me to safety when an enemy bullet struck him in the heart and he died instantly. He talked about you often, about how both of you loved art," said the young man.

Then the soldier handed the man the package he was carrying.

"I know this isn't much; I'm not really a great artist, but I think your son would have wanted you to have this."

The man took the package and opened it. It was a portrait of his son painted by the young soldier. The man stared in awe at the way the soldier had captured the likeness of his son in the painting. He was so drawn to the eyes of his son while his own eyes welled up with tears. He thanked the young soldier and offered to pay him for the painting.

"Oh no, sir, I could never repay what your son did for me. The painting is a gift. I wish I could do more."

The man thanked the young soldier again and with tears in his eyes said, "I wish I could tell you how much this painting means to me. He was my only son and this is the only portrait I have of him in his uniform. This is the most cherished painting I own."

He hugged the young soldier and watched him as he walked from his door and got into the car that was waiting for him. The man immediately hung the portrait over his mantle, then sat and stared at it for a long time, enjoying fond memories of the times he and his son had spent together and reflecting over how proud he was of him.

Every time visitors came to his home after that day, the man would take them to see the portrait of his son before he showed them any of the great works of art he had collected.

A few months later, the wealthy man died. It was rumored that he died of a broken heart over the loss of his son. An auction of his massive collection of expensive paintings was scheduled. Influential people hearing about the auction came from near and far to bid on the priceless paintings. Art collectors were excited about the opportunity to purchase some of the paintings for their collection. All the paintings to be auctioned sat on a platform in front of the room where the auction would take place. Among the paintings was the painting of the wealthy man's son, the painting the young soldier had painted. The auctioneer pounded his gavel signaling the auction was starting. The first painting he held up was the painting of the man's son.

"We will start the bidding with this picture of the son. Who will bid for this painting?"

There was silence from the crowd. No one seemed to think that the portrait of the deceased wealthy man's son was important or expensive enough for them to purchase. There were whispers from the crowd as people wondered why anyone would want to purchase this picture to add to their collection. They didn't feel that it had any value to them. Oh, sure it was valuable to the wealthy man, it was his son; however, they did not share that same sentiment.

Then a voice from the back of the room shouted.

"We want to see the famous paintings. Skip this one."

But the auctioneer persisted.

"Will somebody bid on this painting? Who will start the bidding? Two-hundred dollars, one-hundred dollars, any amount? Will someone start bidding with any amount?"

Another voice shouted angrily.

"We didn't come to see this amateur painting. We came to see the Van Gogh's and the Rembrandts. I can't put something like that in my collection. Get on with the real bids and stop wasting our time."

"Yeah, we want the real paintings!" someone in the crowd shouted.

But still the auctioneer continued.

"The son, the son, who'll take the son?"

Finally, a voice came from the very back of the room. It was the longtime gardener of the wealthy man and his son.

"I'll give you ten dollars for the painting."

Being a poor man, ten dollars was all he could afford. He had come into the house to observe the auction. He had never attended one before. He had stood in the back of the room away from the wealthy people, who had come to bid on the expensive works of art. He wanted to see who would purchase the portrait of the wealthy man's son.

As he watched and waited, he thought about how good the wealthy man and his son had been to him and his family. When he was sick and couldn't work, the son had made sure the gardener and his family had food and their bills were paid. Both father and son had treated the gardener as a friend and a family member instead of as a servant. When the father ate lunch, if he saw the gardener outside working on the grounds of his magnificent estate, he would invite the gardener to sit at his table and eat with him.

At Christmas, the father ensured the gardener's family had a good Christmas. Over the years, he had used his wealth to help the people in his town in general. He had built schools and hospitals, and he had sponsored scholarships for the children, too.

The rich people who could afford the paintings had come to the auction to purchase the expensive art to enrich themselves and to beautify their homes. The gardener wanted to donate the son's picture to the local museum to share it with the world. He wanted everyone who visited the museum to look upon the face of a man who gave his life to help others. He wanted people who came to the museum to gaze upon the face that was captured in a painting by one of the soldiers whose life the son had saved. Just as the father had been drawn to the eyes of his son and marveled at how the young soldier had captured his son's personality, the gardener wanted the world to enjoy this painting in the same manner.

"We have a ten-dollar bid; who will bid twenty dollars? Do I hear twenty dollars?" called the auctioneer.

"Give it to him for ten dollars and let's get on with the bidding. Let's see the masters," shouted a voice from the crowd.

The crowd was becoming increasingly irate. They didn't want the painting of the son. They wanted the more worthy investments for their collections.

The auctioneer pounded the gavel.

"Going once, going twice, sold to the man in the back for ten dollars!"

A man sitting on the second row shouted with annoyance.

"Now, let's get on with the collection!"

The auctioneer laid down his gavel.

"I'm sorry, but the auction is over," he said.

The crowd was confused and agitated.

"What do you mean, 'over'?" someone shouted.

"What about the paintings?" said another person.

"I'm sorry but when I was hired to conduct this auction, I was told of a stipulation in the will. I was not allowed to divulge that stipulation until this time. Only the painting of the son would be auctioned. Whoever bought that painting would inherit the entire estate, including all the paintings. The man who took the son gets everything," said the auctioneer.

The crowd was upset when they realized the mistake they had made. They left the auction angry, but there wasn't anything they could do to change the outcome.

God gave His son over two-thousand years ago to die on the Cross. Much like the auctioneer, His message today is "the Son, the Son, who will take the Son?" You see, whoever takes the Son gets everything. For God so loved the world he gave His only begotten Son, who so ever believeth shall have eternal life—that's love!

The Definition of Poor

One day, the father of a wealthy family took his son on a trip to the country with the express purpose of showing him how poor people live and to realize how blessed he was, having the lifestyle provided to him. They spent a couple of days and nights on the farm of what would be considered a very poor family.

On their return home from their trip, the father asked his son, "What did you think about our trip?"

"It was great, Dad."

"Did you see how poor people live?" the father asked.

"Oh yeah," said the son.

"So, tell me, what have you learned from the trip?" asked the father. "Aren't you glad for the way we live? Aren't you glad your mother and I can afford to provide for you the things you have and can live in a house such as ours?"

The son sat silent for a moment, then answered: "I saw that we have one dog and they had four. We have a pool that reaches to the middle of our garden and they have a creek that has no end. We have imported lanterns in our garden and they have the stars at night. Our patio reaches to our front yard and they have the whole horizon. We have a small piece of land to live on and they have fields that go beyond our sight. We have servants who serve us, but they serve others. We buy our food, but they grow theirs. We have walls around our property to protect us; they have friends to protect them."

The boy's father was speechless.

Then his son added, "Dad, this trip showed me how poor we are."

Isn't perspective a wonderful thing? Makes you wonder what would happen if we all gave thanks for everything we have, instead of worrying about what we don't have.

Barbara A. Robinson

Appreciate every single thing you have, especially your friends!

Who Is Jesus to You?

We often wonder who the man called "Jesus" really is. Who is this man who turned water into wine, made the blind man see, walked on water, and fed a multitude of people with two fish and five loaves of bread? He is many things to different people, but who is He to you, dear reader? When Jesus was hanging on the cross and said, "Father, forgive them for they know not what they do," to whom was He speaking? "He said "Father". Who is "Father?" These are questions that have puzzled me all of my life. My grandfather used to say as he sang a song to me when I was a little girl maybe five or six years old with the following words, "We'll understand it all bye and bye."

Jesus turned water into wine so He could be called a chemist. In physics, He disapproved the law of gravity when He ascended into heaven, and when He walked on water, too. In economics, He disapproved the law of diminishing return by feeding 5,000 people with two fish and five loaves of bread. In medicine, He cured the sick and the blind without administering a single dose of drugs. In history, He is the beginning and the end. In religion, He said no one comes to the Father except through Him. Jesus had no servants, yet He is called Master. He had no degree, yet they called Him Teacher. He had no children, yet He is called Father. He had no medicines, yet He was called Healer. He had no army, yet kings feared Him.

He won no military battles. Yet, He conquered the world. He committed no crime, yet they crucified Him. He was buried in a tomb, yet He lives today.

When the angel of the Lord spoke to Joseph about Mary's soon-to-be-born Son, he told Joseph, "You shall call His name "Jesus", for He will save His people from their sins," (Matthew 1:21).

Jesus means "the Lord saves" and defines both who Jesus is and why He came. He was also called Immanuel, which means "God with us" (1:23). His name reveals our eternal hope, wrote Bill Crowder, a best-selling author with Our Daily Bread Ministries.

Just as we often wonder who Jesus is, we sometimes wonder what to call Him when we pray. So many people call Him by different names. We are puzzled with trying to determine which name is correct. Since Jesus means many things to many people there is no one way to describe Him. But we can say He is an omnipotent presence in our lives. We can look at the influence He has in our lives and call Him according to what His significance is.

Ask yourself, does He keep you from sin? Then call Him "Savior." Does He free you from slavery of your mind and of your passions? Then call Him "Redeemer." Does He teach you as no one else has taught you because He alone knows all things? Then call Him "Teacher." Does He mold and master your life and open doors for you that you never knew were closed and in places where you didn't know there were doors? Then call Him "Master." Does He shine upon the pathway that is dark to you and lead you into the light of your life, a place that gives you hope? Then call Him "Guide." Is He always there when you need Him? Is He steadfast and unchangeable? Then call Him "The Rock of Gibraltar."

Does He bring peace into your life? Then call Him "Comforter." Does He make a way out of no way? Then call Him "Miracle Worker." Does He fill your heart with joy when you're sad? Then call Him "Dr. Happiness." Did He make humankind into his likeness? Then call Him "Creator." Is He omnipotent and the ruler of all? Then call Him "The Supreme Being." Are we His children? Then call Him "Father." When you call Him, He may not come at the moment He's called, but is He ever late? Is He always on time? Then call Him, "Dr. On-Time." Does He reveal God to you? Then call Him "The

Son of God." Does He reveal Man to you? Then call Him "The Son of Man."

In following Him, are your lips silent in your capacity to depict Him and His influence upon you; is it that you just can't find the words to describe the influence Jesus has in your life and on your life or to define who He is? Then just pray and say, "Our Father who art in Heaven," and follow Him, confident in the knowing that you are following the King of Kings who owns the world and everything in it! He is everything!

Your Biggest Opponent

As we go through life, there is always some type of problem that seems to arise. But one thing that I have come to realize is that regardless of what the problem is, the one constant ingredient is me. I am always there before, during, and after my problems. Heck, sometimes I even create them! That being said, I have also come to realize that I am my greatest opponent. I know it sounds harsh and could be a hard pill to swallow, but if you look deeply at your current situation, it is either good or bad because of you. I know that in some cases you aren't to blame for a problem or tragedy; however, you are still connected to it in some manner, such as death, abuse, or some other type of injustice. But, beyond those cases, you are in control of your life and your future. The way you shape your thoughts and your mental habits determine the way you create your life, thus, making you your greatest opponent.

Someone else could hurt you, disrespect you, or even try to control you but ultimately you dictate your own life. They can only inflict those feelings on you if you give them permission to do so. You control your life and you control those behaviors that you allow to control your life. I will give you an example: some people always complain about their jobs or their living situation. However, instead of trying to change the situation, they accept it and continue to complain about it. If you cannot change the situation, change your attitude about the situation.

You might say, "I don't accept my situation," but you have done little or nothing to change it. You might have made a feeble attempt or applied a mediocre solution to lie to yourself and to others that you have tried to change the situation. But the problem isn't the situation; it is you. Nine times out of ten, if your situation is mediocre then your mental state is mediocre, too.

One of the problems with being your biggest opponent is that most people don't even realize it. Here's a quick test: the next time you have a casual conversation with someone and they discuss one of their problems with you, listen to them to see if they also can think of a solution. It may not be the desired solution, but there is a solution.

The conversation usually happens like this: Your friend is telling you about something that has happened to them and then they say, "You see, that's my problem right there." There is usually never another comment saying, "Now, this will be my solution." You see, times like these are when you are hurting yourself subconsciously. Thus, solidifying the fact that you are your greatest opponent.

Ok, here is one more test to show you that you are your biggest opponent. When you are attempting something new or difficult, one of the things that often happens is that you tell yourself, "I can't do this," or "I'm too tired," or "forget this," and, just like that, you actually can't do it, or you are too tired, or you mentally quit. Now, if you say to yourself, "I got this," or "this isn't so bad," or "I'm doing great," you will notice a change.

Try telling yourself something positive every time you wake up, and you will start to see a change in your life. The biggest and best way to use being your biggest opponent in your favor is to simply become your biggest fan. I don't mean to become cocky or self-centered but to become more humble, less wavered, more focused and controlled. Some of the ways to do that are to speak positivity, filter your thoughts, and control your tongue. The latter sometimes proves to be one of the hardest things to do, but it is worth trying.

Nicky's Courage

Muhammad Ali, who was once the heavyweight champion of the world, often visited children in hospitals. He brought cheer to sick children by telling them jokes, talking to them, and playing games with them. While on one such visit to a hospital, he saw a little boy who was wearing a helmet on his head. Ali asked the doctor why the little boy was wearing a helmet.

"That's Nicky. He's seven-years-old and he's probably the bravest little guy I've ever met. He knows that he only has a short time to live but each morning I come into his room, he gives me the brightest smile and asks me how I am feeling," said the doctor.

Nicky looked at Muhammad Ali and smiled.

"You're the champ! How are you doing, champ?" Nicky asked excitedly and held out his hand to shake Ali's.

The doctor told Ali that Nicky had inoperable brain cancer and he would probably live only a few more weeks.

Ali shook the little boy's outstretched hand.

"Wow, I'm really meeting the champ!" the little boy said.

Nicky was proud to meet the heavyweight champion of the world.

"No, *you're* the champ," said Ali.

Ali knelt down so that he could be at eye-level with Nicky.

"I tell you what; in my next fight, I'm going to beat Frazier and you're going to beat that cancer. I'll return to tell you about my victory, and you can tell me about yours. Is that a deal?" Ali said to Nicky.

Nicky smiled at Ali and nodded his head.

"It's a deal, champ," he said.

Two weeks later, Ali visited the hospital again and went to see Nicky. Nicky's condition had gotten worse. It was evident that he wasn't going to win his battle with cancer. Ali asked the doctor about Nicky's condition. The doctor said it was only a matter of days; the cancer had spread too far.

"It's a miracle that he has lasted this long," said the doctor.

Ali walked over to Nicky's bed and, at the sight of Ali, Nicky's big blue eyes lit up with joy. He was excited to see him.

"Hello, champ! I was hoping to get a chance to see you again. I've been waiting for you," he said.

Nicky was so weak he could hardly lift his hand.

Ali tried hard to fight back his tears. He tried to smile at Nicky to give him courage and took the boy's hands in his.

"I told you that I'm going to beat Frazier and you've got to beat your cancer," said Ali.

Nicky smiled at Ali.

"No, champ. I'm going to meet God, and when I get there, I'm gonna tell Him that I know you," said Nicky.

Ali hugged the little boy.

"You're the bravest champ I've ever met and you'll always be my hero," said Ali.

Nicky smiled at Ali, closed his eyes and went to tell God that he had met the champ.

THE END.

ACKNOWLEDGMENTS

There are several people I will thank for making this book possible. Many of my friends and colleagues sent me short stories with profound messages that made me think. Some of them were messages that made me say to myself, "Things are not as bad as they could be." Others made me thank God for my trials and tribulations because someone else's situations or circumstances were a little worse than mine. Some of the ideas I received made me see messages in places where, in similar situations in my past life, I hadn't seen the lesson that the incident or issue was presenting to me at the time. Some stories made me laugh and others encouraged me to have confidence in myself.

I thank my copy editor, Effrosyni Moschoudi, who edited my manuscript and provided me with valuable suggestions as to how to best make this book enjoyable for the readers.

To my daughter, Jericka, a simple "Thank you," would never be enough to show my gratitude for her tireless and unselfish contributions to, not only this book, but to everything I endeavor. I always know that I have at least one fan in my corner. She tells me that I can walk on the moon, and in her mind, I can.

To Jerome, Jr., my son, I offer my sincere thanks for taking care of the day-to-day operations of the family business so that I could be free to pursue my passion of writing. When I started this book, I knew that the majority of my time would be spent writing and rewriting this manuscript. He knew it too, but he said, "Stay at home today, Ma, and write. I'll handle things at the office." Thanks, my son, for being a blessing in my life. It took many years to write this book because each time I began working on the manuscript another idea came into my mind.

A special thanks goes to Jacqueline Holloman, a powerful sister I met on a retreat for women, who became my soul mate. It has been years since she and I last corresponded with each other; she lives in Virginia and I live in Maryland. She used to send me powerful email messages that were so uplifting I wondered every time how she knew I needed that message at that specific moment.

Another thank you goes to my good friend Charles Taylor, a great poet whom I met at the Black Writer's Guild in Baltimore some years ago. Although over the years he and I lost touch with each other, the effects of his writings still encourage and inspire me. Almost every day I eagerly searched my email messages looking for a correspondence from Charles. He always sent me the most beautiful short stories. I don't know from where he would get them. Perhaps someone sent them to him, or perhaps he created some of them with his wonderful, highly imaginative mind. I just know that there have been many days when I was feeling down and depressed and then I would receive a message from Charles and the rest of my day would be filled with cheer. Sounds corny? Yeah, it does. But it's true!

So, thanks to all of you and may you continue to be a blessing to others.

ABOUT THE AUTHOR

Business Consultant; Workforce Development Trainer; Motivational Speaker; Educator; Published Author; Entrepreneur/Business Owner; Political/Community Activist; Radio Talk-show Host; Adjunct College Professor; Curricula Developer

Barbara A. Robinson is the author of this exciting book of fiction. Barbara, a retired Maryland State Senator is a grandmother and great-grandmother and lives in Pikesville, Maryland. She has been writing since she was in the sixth grade.

Much of Barbara's work comes from her life's experiences, her travels to various countries and from her own imagination. Some of her inspiration also comes from stories told to her by her grandparents and other elders in the neighborhood where she grew up in Georgia and Alabama.

Those stories were also told to other neighborhood children when there wasn't school the next day and the supper dishes were washed and put away. During those southern nights the southern moon was shining so bright it appeared that a giant spotlight was shining on the entire neighborhood.

CONTACT INFORMATION

Mailing address: P.O. BOX 7667, Baltimore, Maryland 21207

Email: barbara4025@verizon.net

Website: barbararobinson.info

Tel: 410-486-6219 (Office) –– 410-804-6769 (cell)